# ▶ Word-Attack Basics

**Decoding A
Workbook**

*Siegfried Engelmann • Linda Carnine • Gary Johnson*

**SRA
McGraw-Hill**

*Columbus, Ohio*

*A Division of The **McGraw·Hill** Companies*

**PHOTO CREDITS**
Cover Photo: KS Studios

*SRA/McGraw-Hill*

*A Division of The* **McGraw·Hill** *Companies*

2002 Imprint
Copyright © 1999 by SRA/McGraw-Hill.

Send all inquiries to:
SRA/McGraw-Hill
8787 Orion Place
Columbus, Ohio 43240-4027

Printed in the United States of America.

ISBN 0-02-674773-1

12 13 14 POH 07 06 05

**1**

t    a    s    e    m

___  ___  ___  ___  ___  ___  ___

**2**

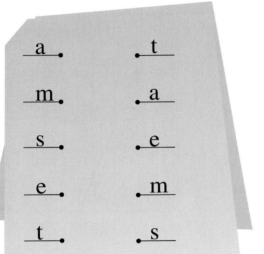

**3**

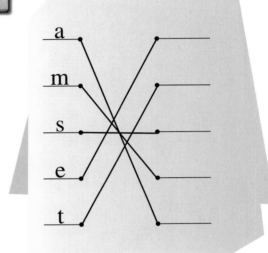

**4**

1. → me    2. → am    3. → ma    4. → eem

**5**

(m)  m  s  a  m  t  e  s  a  m  e  t  a  m  t  s  m  e  t  a  t  m  e  s  s  a
s  t  e  m  a  s  m  a  t  m  s  t  a  m  s  e  t  m  e  m  s  m  e  m  a

(a)  s  t  e  m  a  t  m  e  s  t  m  e  a  s  t  m  a  m  e  s  t  t  a  s  e  t
m  e  s  t  m  a  t  s  a  m  e  t  a  e  m  t  e  a  m  t  a  m  e  s  m  a

(t)  s  e  m  a  s  e  a  t  a  m  e  t  a  s  e  s  e  a  e  s  a  t  e  a  s  t  e
m  s  m  e  t  m  a  m  s  m  e  m  t  a  s  t  m  a  m  s  t  e  m  s

| A | B | C |
|---|---|---|

= ☐

**1**

r　　e　t　　m　　a　　s

＿＿＿＿　＿＿＿＿　＿＿＿＿　＿＿＿＿　＿＿＿＿

＿＿＿＿　＿＿＿＿　＿＿＿＿　＿＿＿＿　＿＿＿＿

**2**

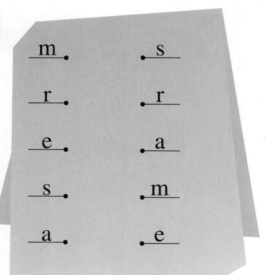

| m | s |
|---|---|
| r | r |
| e | a |
| s | m |
| a | e |

**3**

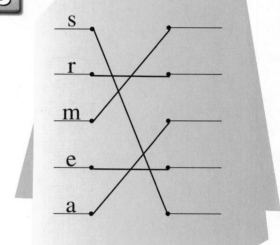

**4**

1. → me　　2. → am　　3. → ree

4. → see　　5. → eem　　6. → ma

**5**

(e) t r e s m a r t e m s a m e t r s r a t e m s a r e t
s m e t a r e m t a s e m s a e m t m e s e a s a e

(a) s t a r e m a s r a m e s e m a m e a t m e a s r
m s a r e r m s m a m e m s m r t a s e a r a m e

(r) a s m e r t e s a t r e s e r t a m s e t m e s a a
r m e s e a m t e r a m s m e r a m t r e m a m s

**1**

d   r   s   e   a   m   t

_____   _____   _____   _____   _____   _____

_____   _____   _____   _____   _____   _____

**2**

1. → ra →    2. → sa →    3. → ees →

4. → ma →    5. → meet →    6. → see →

**3**

| | |
|---|---|
| e | s |
| s | m |
| d | t |
| t | d |
| m | e |

**4**

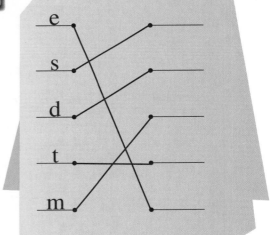

e
s
d
t
m

**5**

(d) e r s d m d r a e t r d m t r a s e d m e d t r a m
    d s t r t r d t r m s d t r m r t d t s t d m e r s d a

(t) d t r a m d r t a d r t r m e r a r t r m a m t m e
    m r a m e t r d e m t r d t r t d d t r e d t a m d

(d) d t r a m d r t m a r a e s t r d e a d r t m t s d r t r a
    m d r t d m a r t r t d r t d m a r t r t d r a m d r t d m

| A | B | C | = | |
|---|---|---|---|---|
| | | | | |

**1**

i   t   e   r   d   s   a   m

\_\_\_\_   \_\_\_\_   \_\_\_\_   \_\_\_\_   \_\_\_\_   \_\_\_\_   \_\_\_\_   \_\_\_\_

\_\_\_\_   \_\_\_\_   \_\_\_\_   \_\_\_\_   \_\_\_\_   \_\_\_\_   \_\_\_\_   \_\_\_\_

**2**

1. sa →   2. sad →   3. sat →

4. mat →   5. ees →   6. me →

7. at →   8. am →   9. ma →

**3**

a •          e \_\_\_\_
s •          i •
i •          t •
t •          a \_\_\_\_
e •          s \_\_\_\_

(1 point)

**4**

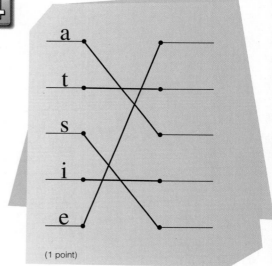

(1 point)

**5**

(i)   m i s r e t i d r d i m a t i s d e m s a i t r d i e s r
a t s i t d i d m a t i s r a i e i r i s t m s r d t i r

(1 point)

(a)   a r a m e a m t e a d e r m a r m e m r t e m d e a
t d a r m a t e d a r t d r a t r m r e a r d r e m

(1 point)

(i)   d t s i e r i d s i a t a r d i m s i s t r i m e s t a r i
d i d m a t i s r a i e i r s t m s i t r d i t i e m t r

(1 point)

| A | B | C |   | = | |
|---|---|---|---|---|---|

**1**

m    r    e    i    d    a    s    t

\_\_\_\_   \_\_\_\_   \_\_\_\_   \_\_\_\_   \_\_\_\_   \_\_\_\_   \_\_\_\_   \_\_\_\_

\_\_\_\_   \_\_\_\_   \_\_\_\_   \_\_\_\_   \_\_\_\_

**2**

1. ad →   2. at →   3. sat →   4. sad →

5. mad →   6. rat →   7. eem →   8. reem →

9. am →   10. ram →   11. sam →

**3**

r •          • d

m •          • t

i •          • r

d •          • i

t •          • m

(1 point)

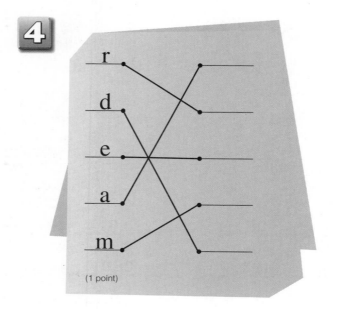

r

d

e

a

m

(1 point)

**5**

(a)

d r t a s i e t a d r a m s t d e r a s r e t a s m r t
a r e a r t a s n t d s r a n d a s t n r e a t d a n s t

(1 point)

(i)

d r i t i r m e i a r i d r i d t i r e a t s m i t e a r i
t e i d r i e m e i a s r i d e t m e a d e i t a r s i s

(1 point)

(a)

s m a r t m e i r i d r a e d e d m a r m a m e a r
t d e a d i t d a r s e m e a s t d i e s d a r i a r i

(1 point)

A B C = 

**1**

    i     e     m     f     r     d     a     t     s

\_\_\_\_ \_\_\_\_ \_\_\_\_ \_\_\_\_ \_\_\_\_ \_\_\_\_ \_\_\_\_ \_\_\_\_ \_\_\_\_

\_\_\_\_ \_\_\_\_ \_\_\_\_ \_\_\_\_ \_\_\_\_ \_\_\_\_ \_\_\_\_ \_\_\_\_

**2**

1. → at →    2. → at →

**3**

1. → im →   2. → if →   3. → it →

4. → sa →   5. → eet →   6. → reem →

7. → fit →   8. → seem →   9. → ad →

10. → fa →   11. → sad →

**4**

●———————→    ●———————→

**5**

| | |
|---|---|
| f | s |
| i | f |
| s | i |
| r | t |
| t | r |
| e | e |

(1 point)

**6**

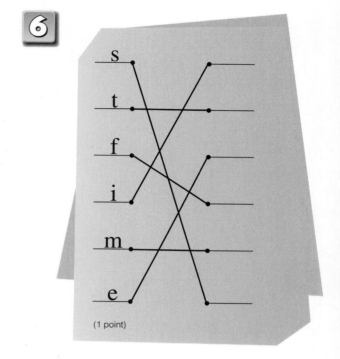

(1 point)

**7**

(f) m f i r d a t s f m i r d f t f d i f m e m e m f t r
f t m f t m f m e m f m e r m e f e r d f e d f e d t
(1 point)

(t) f t i r d f i t m f i t f d f m t m f e r m i r a t s f i t
f t i s f a i s f i t f i t i r m f i r m f s t r s i f r t f
(1 point)

(f) t i r e d f i m f i t i f m a s i f i e m f i d s a s m d i f
t i e m d i f t i e m d i f m e d i f e t f e d f r t r f t f
(1 point)

**1**

d    h    f    a    s    r    i    t    e    m

___  ___  ___  ___  ___  ___  ___  ___  ___  ___

___  ___  ___  ___  ___  ___  ___  ___  ___

**2**

1. —— at ——→    2. —— at ——→    3. —— at ——→

**3**

1. —— if ——→    2. —— at ——→    3. —— mass ——→

4. —— miss ——→    5. —— fee ——→    6. —— feed ——→

7. —— sit ——→    8. —— fat ——→    9. —— rim ——→

10. —— mitt ——→    11. —— seem ——→    12. —— id ——→

**4**

1. ●———————→    2. ●———————→    3. ●———————→

**5**

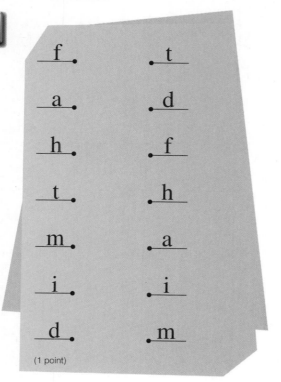

f •       • t

a •       • d

h •       • f

t •       • h

m •       • a

i •       • i

d •       • m

(1 point)

**6**

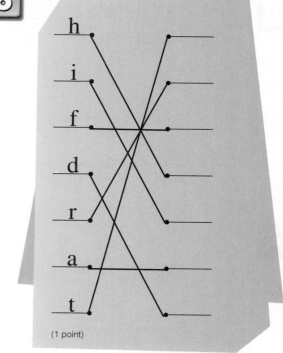

h
i
f
d
r
a
t

(1 point)

**7**

(i) d r m i f i d i d i h r a t e a h e f i t i f m r a e r s r d
i t i f m r t r f t d i t t s f i t m e t i m e r i f t i m
(1 point)

(h) a d h r t e r i s m d r h s m h i s e f h t f r f h t m
e r d f h s a t e h t e r f i f t h s t i s h a m e h i
(1 point)

(t) e t s h s m h t r e h i f h r m r e h t f a d t h e m
s d i h t i m e r s t d e f i d t r i m e t s f h e a f
(1 point)

**1**

_____ _____ _____ _____ _____ _____ _____ _____

_____ _____ _____ _____ _____ _____ _____ _____

**2**

1. eed → 2. eed →

**3**

1. me → 2. see → 3. mid →

4. seem → 5. miss → 6. sit →

7. rim → 8. ram → 9. fat →

10. mitt →

**4**

1. ●———→ 2. ●———→ 3. ●———→

**5**

| | |
|---|---|
| i. | .c |
| s. | .e |
| r. | .i |
| c. | .t |
| e. | .s |
| d. | .d |
| t. | .r |

(1 point)

**6**

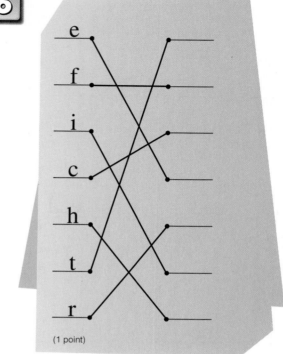

(1 point)

**7**

ⓒ   s f c e r i t a m c t a r c f d e i c t a m i d c t r c e
(1 point)   h f c h c s i c d e f d c i d e c r i f t c d e r i m s

ⓓ   f d h t i s i e h t h s d h e h t f e i d h e a h s e h
(1 point)   f t i d h e t i f d h e i t h f i e d s h e h a s e d e i

ⓒ   s f c a r e a m e t t h r e d c e t a c d e t i f s h e
(1 point)   c a e f t h e h s e c s e h s a c a e f h t c e h c a h

**1**

_____ _____ _____ _____ _____ _____ _____ _____

_____ _____ _____ _____ _____ _____ _____ _____

(1 point)

**2**

1. ad→     2. ad→

**3**

1. me→     2. see→     3. mad→     4. rid→

5. am→     6. ham→     7. reed→

**4**

1. ●———→     2. ●———→     3. ●———→

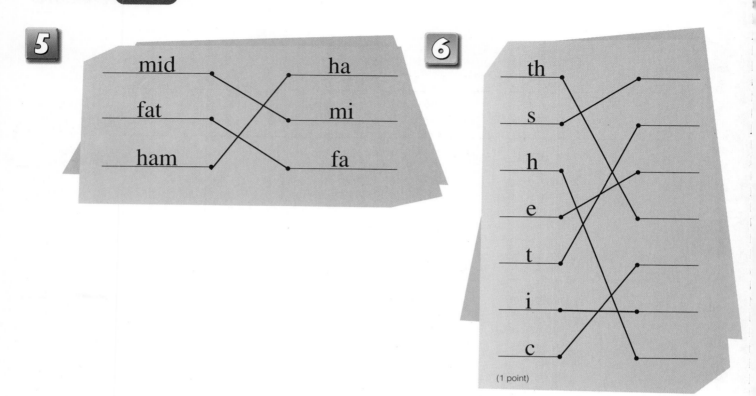

**5**

mid      ha

fat      mi

ham      fa

**6**

th

s

h

e

t

i

c

(1 point)

**7**

(t) t f i e h d t h f h e d h a i s h f t h f h e d h e d h
(1 point) e i f h t i e h f i t h e i f a s h d h e i t h f e i d h

(f) f i e d h e i f t h e i d i f e i f e i d h e h d a h e d
(1 point) i e f e h d t i e h f e t f t e h d f i e t f e a s h e i f

(h) e h d i f h e i s i f h e i d i f h t e i d h e t s a d h
(1 point) e t f h e f h d h a h e d h e t f i e h d i t h e d i a

| A | B | C |
|---|---|---|
|   |   |   |

= 

**1**

_____  _____  _____  _____  _____  _____  _____  _____  _____

_____  _____  _____  _____  _____  _____  _____  _____  _____

(1 point)

**2**

1. eet →    2. eet →

**3**

1. reef →    2. this →    3. that →    4. at →

5. mat →    6. mad →    7. mast →    8. if →

9. hit →    10. feed →

**4**

1. →    2. →    3. →

**5**

sid        fi
fit        si
me        m

**6**

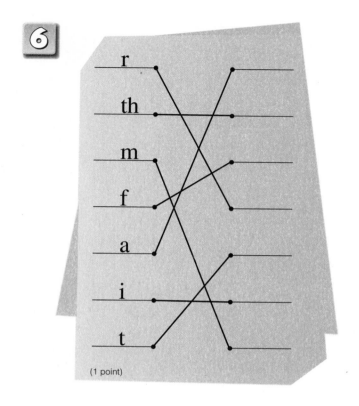

(1 point)

**7**

(th)
(1 point)
r i t h s i f h e s a t h e f h t s t h f h e h s h e h t h
e s h t h f e h t f h t h f e t e f h t f h e t h f e s

(h)
(1 point)
r t h a m e n a t m e a d e f e n h e m a s i e n f
h e m t h a n s m e n f h t e n a s m t n f h e n s

(t)
(1 point)
r i t h a m e n f h e d t h d i e d a n f m e n d t h
f e n d m e t n f h e n d e t d a e t e h f m e t h

**1**

_____  _____  _____  _____  _____  _____  _____

_____  _____  _____  _____  _____  _____

(1 point)

**2**

1. ⟶ it    2. ⟶ it

**3**

1. ⟶ feed    2. ⟶ reef    3. ⟶ had    4. ⟶ hid

5. ⟶ hat    6. ⟶ that    7. ⟶ this    8. ⟶ the

9. ⟶ cam    10. ⟶ cat

**4**

1. ⟶    2. ⟶    3. ⟶

**5**

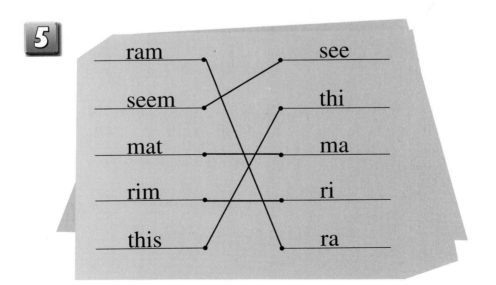

ram          see

seem         thi

mat          ma

rim          ri

this         ra

**6**

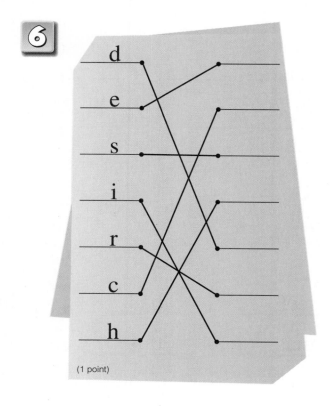

d
e
s
i
r
c
h

(1 point)

**7**

(th) r i m t h s c i e l t h s i e h f e h s h e t f e h t h f
e t d h t h f e h t e i d l s d i f t h e f h e i t h f e
(1 point)

(th) m t h i s h t h e l s s i f h t h e i f h t e i f h e s
t h e i f h e h t l f m e n t h e f n e a h t h t n e h f
(1 point)

(th) n e t h e f e t n t h m f h t e n f m t h e f n e t m
f h t e t h s h e t h n e m t n e t h m e t h e m e
(1 point)

**1**

_____ _____ _____ _____ _____ _____ _____

_____ _____ _____ _____ _____ _____ _____

(1 point)

**2**

1. ———am———→    2. ———am———→

**3**

1. ———ham———→    2. ———cat———→    3. ———hat———→    4. ———the———→

5. ———rim———→    6. ———that———→    7. ———fees———→

8. ———rid———→    9. ———mast———→

**4**

1. ●————————→    2. ●————————→    3. ●————————→

**5**

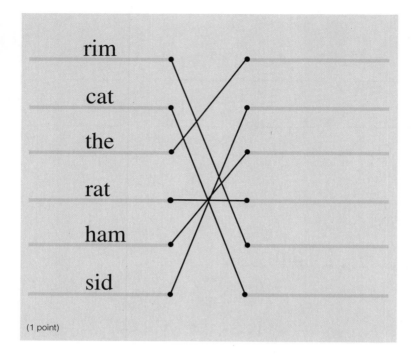

rim

cat

the

rat

ham

sid

(1 point)

**6**

(h) m e n t h m e n t h e n f d h e n f m e n t h e n
(1 point)  s m e n d h e m n f t m e n d h s n e m d n t h f

(th) m e t h d n e f m t f i t h s h i h t h f i e h f h t h
(1 point)  e f t e h f n e m t h e n f m e d n f i e h t h d i e

(t) t h e l d m i a n d i e h f t n e d e f e e d m e n t h
(1 point)  f d n e t m e t h d i e f t d f e d f i t h e d l f i t

**1**

_____  _____  _____  _____  _____  _____  _____

_____  _____  _____  _____  _____  _____

(1 point)

**2**

1. ———at———→    2. ———at———→    3. ———at———→

**3**

1. ———she———→    2. ———dad———→    3. ———rid———→    4. ———did———→

5. ———sad———→    6. ———hams———→    7. ———seem———→

8. ———rims———→    9. ———sham———→

**4**

1. ●————————→    2. ●————————→    3. ●————————→

**5**

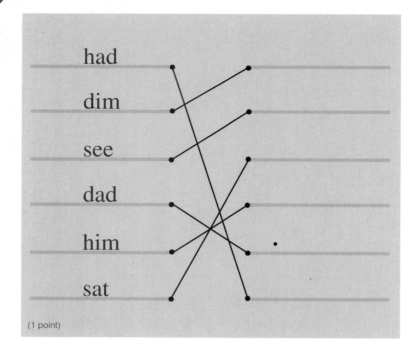

had

dim

see

dad

him

sat

(1 point)

**6**

(sh) a r s t h s h t h e h s h e h t h f d s d h e s h e t f
h e s h t f e s d e f s h t h f h e s d e s f h s t s h
(1 point)

(th) a r t h s i e s h i f t h f i e d h f e d t h f e h d h a
s f t h e d f e f d t h s f h t d t h f h e h f h t e f t
(1 point)

(sh) s i e h f s h e m t h e s h f t h e f n e s d e f s h
f h t e n f s h f s f e n d s h e f m e t s h f e n s
(1 point)

**1**

_____  _____  _____  _____  _____  _____

_____  _____  _____  _____  _____  _____

(1 point)

**2**

1. ———it———→  2. ———it———→

**3**

1. ———he———→  2. ———this———→  3. ———hats———→  4. ———did———→

5. ———rams———→  6. ———that———→  7. ———him———→  8. ———the———→

9. ———reefs———→  10. ———she———→

**4**

1. •————————→  2. •————————→  3. •————————→

**5**

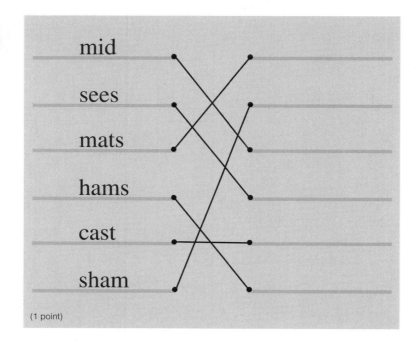

mid

sees

mats

hams

cast

sham

(1 point)

**6**

 **sh**

(1 point)

t h s h f h e s h f e s f e d d s d s h t h f e s s l f
h e h s d h d e h s h f e h d h s h e h f h e h s h f

**th**

(1 point)

r i t h s l s m e n s h t e n f m s t h e f e m s e n
t h f e m s n e f t h e n f d e d t h f e n d f h t e d

**sh**

(1 point)

l s f e h s h f e s h f e t h f h s h d e n f h e l d
m e s n e m d h s n e h s f n e s h e m s n e f s h e

**1**

_____  _____  _____  _____  _____  _____

_____  _____  _____  _____  _____  _____

(1 point)

**2**

1. id 2. id

**3**

1. tim  2. rats  3. cad  4. dim

5. he  6. shim  7. cast  8. fist

9. she  10. reefs  11. that  12. cats

13. sheet

**4**

1. ⟶  2. ⟶  3. ⟶

**5**

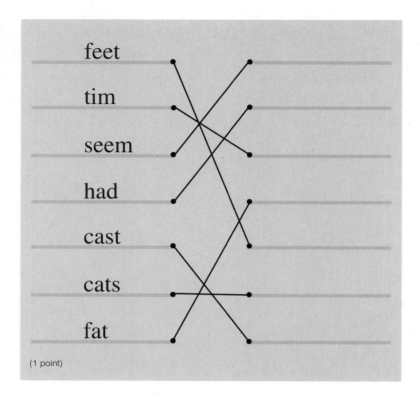

feet

tim

seem

had

cast

cats

fat

(1 point)

**6**

(n)
m n r e n r m e a r t n s m t h s n e m n t f t m e
a t n e m s n t a h s e r t m e n r m e n t r m s e
(1 point)

(sh)
t h i s h e i f h s h e h f d t h s d t h s t s h t e i f
h s h e f s d f s h e t s h t f d s d t s h m f e s n r
(1 point)

(th)
s h e e t h f i s h e f t h i d r i m r i t h r t d t e s
n e t h f m e n t h s e h e f h s d t h t f e d f h d s
(1 point)

**1**

_____  _____  _____  _____  _____  _____  _____

_____  _____  _____  _____  _____  _____  _____

(1 point)

**2**

1. ⟶ eem  2. ⟶ eem

**3**

1. ⟶ fist  2. ⟶ fit  3. ⟶ fits  4. ⟶ cats

5. ⟶ me  6. ⟶ can  7. ⟶ cast  8. ⟶ fast

9. ⟶ dim  10. ⟶ din  11. ⟶ an  12. ⟶ tan

13. ⟶ sheets

**4**

1. ⟶  2. ⟶  3. ⟶

**5**

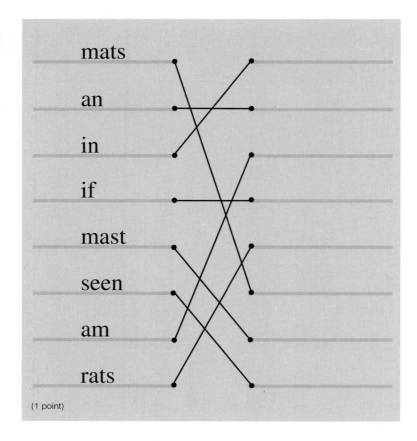

mats
an
in
if
mast
seen
am
rats

(1 point)

**6**

 **(th)**

f t i t h s f h t e t h f s e d i f h t e f t h f s e d e
t h f e d f s a e t h e d f f s h t e f t h e f d e t h f e

(1 point)

**(n)**

m n e r m e n r n e m s a n e m s r e n c n e r t
n e n d m h e n m d n e h d n e m e n t r n e m

(1 point)

**(sh)**

t h i s h f i s h f h e h d t h e d s h e d h s h e d s
f s h t h s f h t e s h f e h s e s d t f s h t e d a e

(1 point)

**1**

_____  _____  _____  _____  _____  _____

_____  _____  _____  _____  _____  _____

(1 point)

**2**

1.  ad    2.  ad 

**3**

1.  sat     2.  fish     3.  ram     4.  ran 

5.  dim     6.  din     7.  feet     8.  feed 

9.  he     10.  him     11.  she     12.  had 

13.  fast     14.  cats 

**4**

1. •————————▶    2. •————————▶    3. •————————▶

**5**

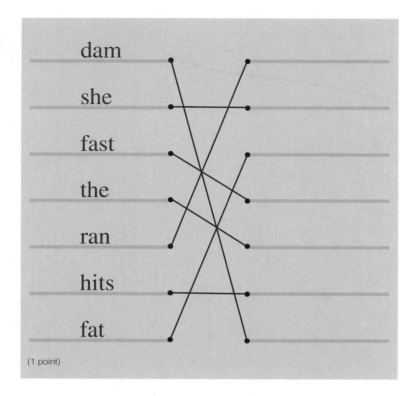

dam

she

fast

the

ran

hits

fat

(1 point)

**6**

(sh)
t h f s h i f d t h s t i f s h t e d s h s t h e d f s d
t s h t e i s h t i f d i s h e d f s h t s f t i s h e d s
(1 point)

(n)
m e n t h s n t h e s e n t m e n t h s n e r e n t
m r n e m r n t e m s n e a n s n e m r i m e n e
(1 point)

(th)
m e t h d i s h t h e f i s h d i d t h e s h e t d f h
t f t h f h t i s m e r e t h r d t r h t d t h e h s t h
(1 point)

| A | B | C | | = | |
|---|---|---|---|---|---|
| | | | | | |

**1**

_____ _____ _____ _____ _____ _____

_____ _____ _____ _____ _____ _____

(1 point)

**2**

1. ———→ in    2. ———→ in

**3**

1. ———→ is    2. ———→ can    3. ———→ dim    4. ———→ ash

5. ———→ mad    6. ———→ feet    7. ———→ she    8. ———→ he

9. ———→ had    10. ———→ ram    11. ———→ seem    12. ———→ him

13. ———→ did    14. ———→ need

**4**

1. ●————————→    2. ●————————→    3. ●————————→

**5**

———→ She had rats and cats. ———→

**6**

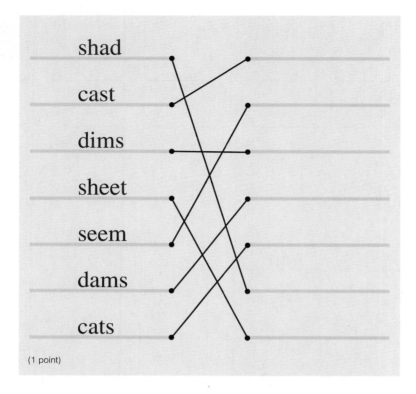

shad

cast

dims

sheet

seem

dams

cats

(1 point)

**7**

(h)
f d h t h e f i s h d e h d h e t f e s h d e h t h d
h e t h d i e h d i s h e i t i f s e r h e m s n e n r
(1 point)

(sh)
t h i s h f i d s h a d f h s t i s f t s n t h s h e i d
i f s h e h t i f i s h e t s n m h s h e t n e s h m h
(1 point)

(th)
f i s t h d i f h t i m t h s i f h e i t h s h e n m e
d f h e h t d t h e d m e n t h s e i f h t h s t h t s
(1 point)

**1**

_____  _____  _____  _____  _____  _____

_____  _____  _____  _____  _____

(1 point)

**2**

1. ___eed→   2. ___eed→

**3**

1. ___am→   2. ___if→   3. ___an→   4. ___it→

5. ___ash→   6. ___the→   7. ___has→   8. ___fast

9. ___she→   10. ___in→   11. ___cats→   12. ___fins→

13. ___hits→   14. ___he→   15. ___is→   16. ___that→

**4**

1. ●━━━━━▶   2. ●━━━━━▶   3. ●━━━━━▶

**5**

A fish has fins. →

**6**

1. → ma  2. → ma  3. → ca  4. → ca

**7**

mats

sat

had

sit

mast

sad

feed

(1 point)

**8**

(o)

(1 point)

c o a e s o a s t h a o s e h t m e n o a h s e n a o
e h s n i o c e c o i c o a s o e i s o e t h s n e m

(th)

(1 point)

m i t h r i d s h e e t h r h t f t h i f h e i d h t h d
i f e t d i r f r t h d i t h d t d r f t h f d h t i f t h

(sh)

(1 point)

s h o r e d i s h t h i n f a s h t d e o s i f h t s s h t
h e d h s t e s h f h t h e s h f h t h e h i f s h t e

A  B  C  = 

**1**

_____  _____  _____  _____  _____  _____

_____  _____  _____  _____  _____  _____

(1 point)

**2**

1. ——— an ———→    2. ——— an ———→

**3**

the        and        this        ant  ————→

hand       deed       fish        did  ————→

fast       she        fins        cats ————→

cans       has        that             ————→

**4**

1. ●————————→    2. ●————————→    3. ●————————→

**5**

That ram can feed a fish. ————————————→

**6**

1. ⟶ ma ⟶   2. ⟶ ca ⟶   3. ⟶ fee ⟶   4. ⟶ see ⟶

**7**

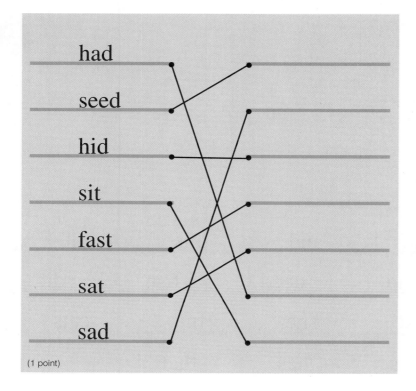

had

seed

hid

sit

fast

sat

sad

(1 point)

**8**

**sh**   s h a d t h s d t h e s h e d o e s h e d t s f t e s h
f e t f s h e f h s t s h t e d s d e s h t s n e t s h
(1 point)

**o**   c o a e c i t h s o i e i s o e i s c a s i e o s i a o s
e i a i s e o s i a i s o i e o a s c o e i c e o c e i a
(1 point)

**th**   t h s d i t h e s h t s h t h i s h t f s h t f t h s e h
f h t e t h f i s t h e i f t d t h e d f t h e s o e h s t
(1 point)

| A | B | C | | |
|---|---|---|---|---|
| | | | = | |

**1**

_____  _____  _____  _____  _____  _____

_____  _____  _____  _____  _____  _____

(1 point)

**2**

1. ●——————▶    2. ●——————▶

**3**

need        this        fast        fist        ——————▶

hand        seems        rims        had        ——————▶

dish        dash        and        cash        ——————▶

that        hats        did        ——————▶

**4**

1. ●——————▶    2. ●——————▶    3. ●——————▶

**5**

His cats ran fast.

**6**

1. → see → 2. → tha → 3. → fi → 4. → fi →

**7**

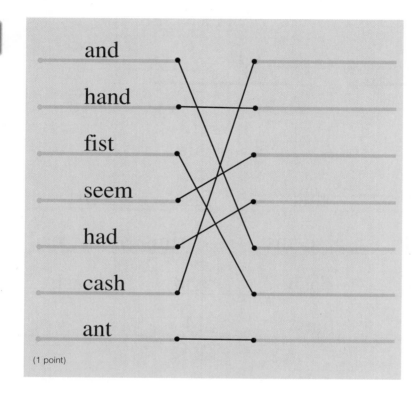

and

hand

fist

seem

had

cash

ant

(1 point)

**8**

(i)  l i t h s i s h f t h s i d f e i d h f t h e i f i d l s i
d h e f h d i e f h e a d i h s l d i e h f i s h d i e h
(1 point)

(o)  o s o a o s c o a o s d i a o s t o a s o t l a s i o e
d a o s n e m s i a c i e a o c i s a n c o e i s n a c
(1 point)

(sh)  s h a i f l s h a i f h s l a h s i f h s h a f h s l a d
s h e i d s h a s l e i s h a i f d e d i t s h a f l i s e
(1 point)

A  B  C  =

**1**

_____  _____  _____  _____  _____  _____

_____  _____  _____  _____  _____  _____

(1 point)

**2**

1. _____  2. _____

**3**

h<u>i</u>m        m<u>a</u>th        <u>t</u>eeth        d<u>i</u>d

d<u>a</u>sh       <u>c</u>ash        <u>d</u>ish        <u>sh</u>e

<u>c</u>ast       n<u>o</u>t         no<u>d</u>         <u>th</u>e

c<u>o</u>n        c<u>a</u>n         <u>an</u>d

**4**

1. _____  2. _____  3. _____

**5**

That ram sat on an ant.

# LESSON 22

## 6

1. _____si_____ 2. _____fi_____ 3. _____cat_____

4. _____nee_____ 5. _____ha_____

## 7

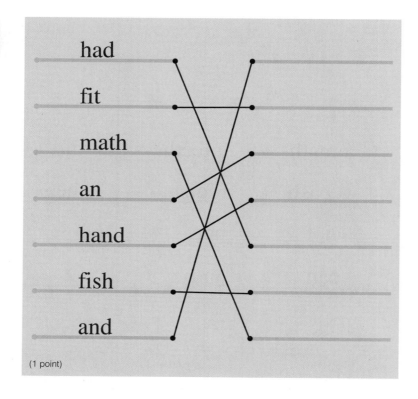

had

fit

math

an

hand

fish

and

(1 point)

## 8

(th)
(1 point)

t h s i d l s i d h e d t f h d e t h f h d h e s i d l e
i f t h d e l f i d e t h d i e f i d h e f t h e i d l f t

(g)
(1 point)

t h g i s l i f h s e i d c a l d i h e m g h d s m e h
t g h c d m e h t s g h c m a s h e g c g h s i e m

(sh)
(1 point)

t h s i f h s i d s h e i f l s i d h s h e h d i f s d e
d s h f e i d f s h e i f a s l s h d i e s g d s h e i d

**1**

_____  _____  _____  _____  _____  _____

_____  _____  _____  _____  _____  _____

(1 point)

**2**

1. _____  2. _____  3. _____

**3**

| | | | | |
|---|---|---|---|---|
| r<u>i</u>ms | s<u>ee</u>n | r<u>a</u>ms | <u>f</u>eet | |
| <u>c</u>ast | <u>h</u>and | t<u>a</u>n | <u>c</u>ash | <u>h</u>ands |
| d<u>i</u>sh | t<u>i</u>n | h<u>a</u>d | sh<u>ee</u>ts | |
| <u>t</u>een | <u>i</u>f | <u>o</u>n | sh<u>o</u>t | |

**4**

1. _____  2. _____  3. _____

**5**

1. She has cats.

2. He needs a tin dish.

3. It is in the hand.

**6**

1. ___hee___    2. ___tha___    3. ___di___    4. ___tha___

**7**

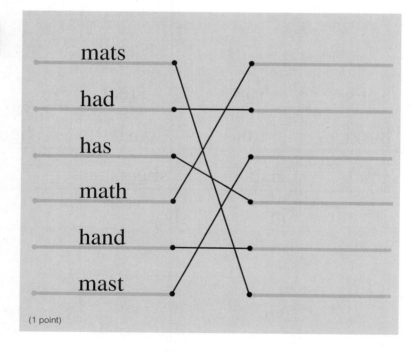

mats

had

has

math

hand

mast

(1 point)

**8**

(c)  o c a o s o e o c o s o e t h a o s n e m a c n s e
(1 point)  m c n e s o a o e s c n e o s c o s e a n s o c o s o

(o)  o a n d e m a d n c m e a n d o c o a m e d c o a
(1 point)  d c o a h e s o c o e a h t o s c a o s c h e o s h

(th)  t h s i e m s i e h t s t h d i s s h e t h e i d l d f h
(1 point)  t e h t h e i d t h d a h d t h d l e a n d m t h e d

A | B | C = ___



1

______ ______ ______ ______ ______ ______

______ ______ ______ ______ ______ ______

(1 point)

2

1. ______ 2. ______ 3. ______

3

mass math than this that

the teeth seems mist dad

feed did sheets reefs deed

4

1. ______ 2. ______ 3. ______

5

1. A shad can not sing.

2. Dad did math.

3. She can see that reef.

6

1. _____shee_____  2. _____mis_____  3. _____fas_____  4. _____ha_____

7

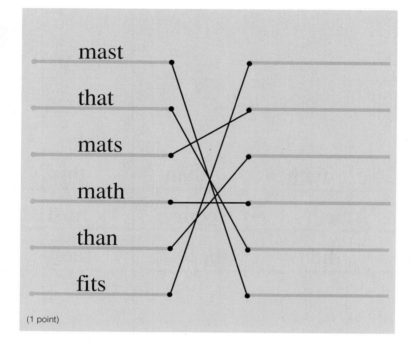

mast

that

mats

math

than

fits

(1 point)

8

(f)
f i g t h e d f h e d h f h d h e h s h f e i d l e i f s
h e i f l a s o r h s o r i f h s h e h  f i e s h a l s i
(1 point)

(th)
t h d i h t d i t h f h t e f h d e f t h e i d l f i e h
s d h t h f h e i f i l s i d h t h f e h s i f l e t d t f
(1 point)

(g)
g i g f i d s d g i d h e i f a r a g h s i c h e g h a i
s h g c h a i e c h g l a o g h s i e o c h g i e s g s
(1 point)

A  B  C  =

**1**

_____  _____  _____  _____  _____  _____

_____  _____  _____  _____  _____  _____

(1 point)

**2**

1. _____  2. _____  3. _____

**3**

cat<u>s</u>       sheet<u>s</u>       ca<u>s</u>t       m<u>a</u>th

mat<u>s</u>       da<u>m</u>       <u>s</u>ees       fee<u>t</u>

fee<u>d</u>       di<u>m</u>       di<u>n</u>       d<u>a</u>n

**4**

1. _____  2. _____  3. _____

**5**

1. She had a shad.

2. That dash is fast.

3. He has rats and cats.

**6**

1. ___da___    2. ___tha___    3. ___di___    4. ___tha___

**7**

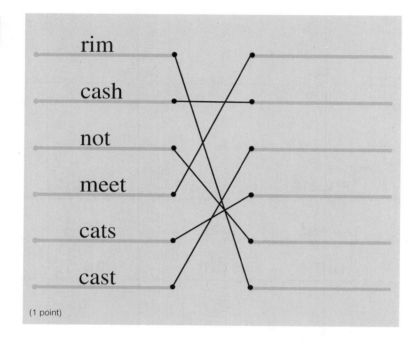

rim

cash

not

meet

cats

cast

(1 point)

**8**

(sh)    s h t i h s i f h g i e h s l f i s h f i s d e t h s i s h t
(1 point)    h s t f i l s h f e i f l s i f h e i s h f i h s i f l s h i

(g)    g a r o a i c o a i c o t h a l c g h s m e s h a m e
(1 point)    n a g h a m a h g m e i a c h g m o c h g o a c h

(o)    o a r i o a i r o c i e o c o e i t h a o d l t h e i m
(1 point)    a n d i o e o a i d n e l t o a d h t i a o e c i e o s

**1**

1. _____ 2. _____ 3. _____ 4. _____

(2 points)

**2**

1. _____ 2. _____ 3. _____

**3**

_____ _____ _____ _____ _____ _____

_____ _____ _____ _____ _____ _____

(1 point)

**4**

sh<u>ee</u>ts    f<u>i</u>ts    c<u>a</u>ts    ham<u>s</u>    fa<u>s</u>t →

da<u>m</u>    d<u>i</u>n    see<u>s</u>    mat<u>s</u>    fee<u>d</u> →

da<u>n</u>    fee<u>t</u>    d<u>i</u>m    <u>sh</u>ad    <u>f</u>ees →

**5**

1. She did not see him.

2. That fish has a fin.

3. A cat had sand on his feet.

4. She hid in the hen shed.

**6**

1. _____ thi _____   2. _____ rat _____   3. _____ hi _____   4. _____ sho _____

**7**

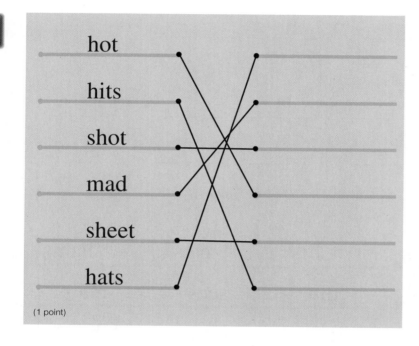

hot

hits

shot

mad

sheet

hats

(1 point)

**8**

(n) m n o i s n f o e i f o n f m e n t l f i t h n m e n
t r m r n r m e   n r a r i e f m r n f m s n r m s a

(g) g o i a o s o i f h t o i f h a g o a h e i r a h r o m
f n e o r m f h e o f g m r o r h e m r n a f g m f

(d) d o r h e o t h e t l a h d f o e h f h t n e m d h
e n t m d n e h t m a d h t h e n d l f m t n e h a

(1 point)

50   LESSON 26

Copyright © SRA/McGraw-Hill

**1**

1. _____   2. _____   3. _____

4. _____   5. _____

(2 points)

**2**

1. _____   2. _____   3. _____

**3**

___ ___ ___ ___ ___ ___

___ ___ ___ ___ ___ ___

(1 point)

**4**

n<u>o</u>t        mo<u>d</u>        h<u>o</u>t        <u>o</u>dd

i<u>f</u>        i<u>n</u>        <u>a</u>n        an<u>d</u>

o<u>n</u>        i<u>t</u>        mi<u>s</u>t        tha<u>n</u>

tha<u>t</u>        <u>t</u>eeth        r<u>i</u>ms        <u>s</u>and

**5**

1. Can she see if it is dim?

2. She met him and me.

3. He met them on the ant hill.

**6**

1. _____ fi _____  2. _____ fi _____  3. _____ thi _____  4. _____ tha _____

**7**

shots

mast

seems

math

fits

hand

(1 point)

**8**

(th) g o i t h e i h t o i t h l f m e n t h s h t e l f h t h
s h e h f i e l d s h t h f h e i d s f h t i e l t f h i

(t) t i f l e i d l o s i f h e i f l t i e o f h t e i d s o d l
f i e h f t h e i f l t o e f i t h e i f o t e l f t h t o f

(d) d h e h t i d l a h d h e l t h d i r l d h e a h d i e
l d a l f i e h s o d i e h f a l d i s h e h f i e d l g

(1 point)

| A | B | C |
|---|---|---|
|   |   |   |

= [ ]

**1**

1. _____   2. _____   3. _____

4. _____   5. _____

(2 points)

**2**

1. _____   2. _____   3. _____

**3**

_____  _____  _____  _____  _____

_____  _____  _____  _____  _____

(1 point)

**4**

| t<u>ee</u>n | ha<u>n</u>d | k<u>i</u>ss | k<u>ee</u>n | k<u>i</u>n |

| <u>s</u>and | mee<u>k</u> | s<u>ee</u>k | s<u>i</u>ck | mi<u>n</u>t |

| g<u>o</u>t | <u>ga</u>sh | d<u>i</u>m | <u>r</u>im | <u>d</u>eed |

**5**

1. He had cash in his hand.

2. Did she see the deed?

3. Ten wet rats sat in the mash.

**6**

1. _____ th _____   2. _____ th _____   3. _____ th _____   4. _____ th _____

**7**

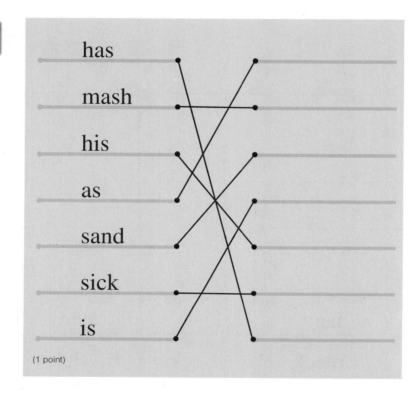

has

mash

his

as

sand

sick

is

(1 point)

**8**

(k)  h t i s k f i l s a l f i s k s h e i f l k a l s k f n e k
a l r i e h a n f i k e n a l s k f i e h t n f k t h s k

(g)  g o a i s o c i a o o g i c i a o e m c a i e i t h a i o
g o a s i o f h e g a o e i d h g l e m a s n e g h o c a

(sh) t h i a l s i h s h e i a l s h e i d l s h a l d i e h a
(1 point) l s h d l i e h t s h a l s l k e h s h e i a s k e t h s

**1**

1. _____  2. _____  3. _____

4. _____  5. _____  6. _____

(2 points)

**2**

1. _____  2. _____  3. _____

**3**

_____  _____  _____  _____  _____

_____  _____  _____  _____  _____

(1 point)

**4**

did      dad      deed      mint      sheets

fins     kiss     kit       ash       odd      sod

sin      sash     seems     math      mash

**5**

1. Can she sit on ten tan mats?

2. An ant is not fast in the dash.

3. She got sand and ants in the dish.

**6**

1. _____ fi _____  2. _____ th _____  3. _____ ra _____  4. _____ ha _____

**7**

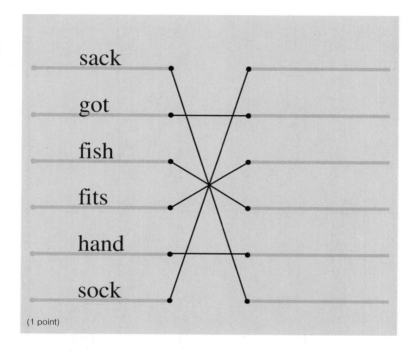

sack

got

fish

fits

hand

sock

(1 point)

**8**

(ck)  c k t h s l c k s i d h c h t i d l c h c k t h s i a k c
h i d c k c d l a k d s e k c k a l s h d c d t h c k h

(n)  m a n o n s o m e n a o s l e m a n s f l e h m a l s
m f r n t l e m a s l m f e n s l a i s o f n e t m l t

(sh)  s h t i s h s l s h c l s h d i d c h a l i d c h s l s h
d i t h c t s h c l a i s d e i s l c h s h c l a h e s d
(1 point)

A B C = 

**1**

1. _____    2. _____    3. _____

4. _____    5. _____    6. _____

(2 points)

**2**

1. _____    2. _____    3. _____

**3**

_____  _____  _____  _____  _____  _____

_____  _____  _____  _____  _____  _____

(1 point)

**4**

| r̲im | t̲rim | s̲a̲sh | t̲r̲ee | ro̲d |
|-----|------|------|------|-----|

| t̲r̲od | ca̲d | co̲d | ki̲d | ki̲ck̲ |
|------|-----|-----|-----|------|

| si̲ck | sa̲ck | tha̲n | thi̲s̲ | r̲ags |
|------|------|------|------|------|

**5**

1. Did he get mad at his cats?

2. Can she kick that sack?

**6**

1. ___th___    2. ___da___    3. ___th___

4. ___sh___    5. ___see___

**7**

She had 3 fish.

This fish is a shad.

This fish is a cod.

This fish is in the cat.

**8**

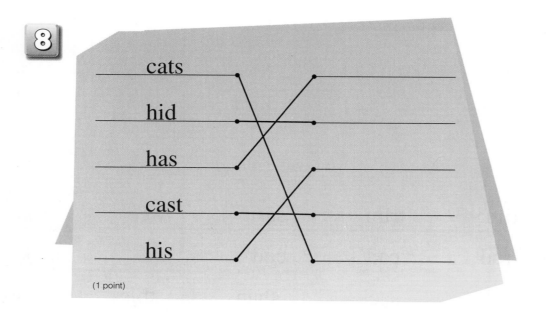

cats

hid

has

cast

his

(1 point)

**9**

d  t h d i e l s o d i c l a h s i c h e i d l s i s o l e d h
   c i d l s i c h g h s i s d l e i d h g h s i o d s l e c

ck  c k t h d i f h g c a l s k d i c f l d c k d i f h o a k
    d c d t c k d i s l c k d i a l s i c k a l s c k e i t h c

g  o a k g l s h r h d n m g n s m e n g l a i s h g n e
   l t h s e n t l g m s o a l s e m g n a h l s e i l t h
(1 point)

**1**

1. _____  2. _____  3. _____

4. _____  5. _____  6. _____

(2 points)

**2**

1. _____  2. _____  3. _____

**3**

_____  _____  _____  _____

_____  _____  _____  _____

(1 point)

**4**

rim     tree     tag     trim     rocks →

kicks     met     send     get     mend →

kids     sacks     men     tin     ten     deed →

**5**

1. He did his math as he sat on the mat.

2. Did she get a cast on the leg?

**6**

1. ____fi____  2. ____see____  3. ____ca____

4. ____shee____  5. ____da____

**7**

He did math.

He did this. (1 + 3 = 5)

Then he did this. (7 + 2 = 4)

Can he add?

**8**

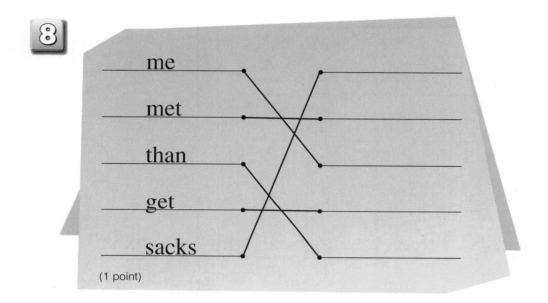

me

met

than

get

sacks

(1 point)

**9**

(ck) c k s h t l e h s l c d l s l s c k d a l s c k a l s k c k
s h e l a h s i t l s o f c k s l s c f l s c k t h e i a c

(sh) s h t l e h s f l s i e h s f s h e l s i f h s l c l a m
c s h c l a m s l c o e h s h c a i e l s h l a i d l s i

(th) t h a l s i e h a m s n t h e a l i s e h t s l a i s t h
s l a i s h e m d c h t h d i a l d h t i d l a t h d l

(1 point)

A | B | C | = | | **LESSON** 32

**1**

_____ _____ _____ _____ _____ _____

_____ _____ _____ _____ _____ _____

(1 point)

**2**

1. _____ 2. _____ 3. _____

4. _____ 5. _____ 6. _____

(2 points)

**3**

d<u>a</u>d    d<u>i</u>d    <u>we</u>    me<u>n</u>    men<u>d</u>

s<u>ee</u>n    s<u>e</u>nt    w<u>i</u>th    m<u>e</u>t    m<u>ee</u>t

sock<u>s</u>    <u>wh</u>en    sen<u>d</u>    ra<u>ck</u>

**4**

1. Can she sit and fish in the mist?

2. Did sand get in the street?

**5**

1. _____ eet _____    2. _____ ca _____    3. _____ ash _____

4. _____ fi _____    5. _____ and _____    6. _____ ad _____

Copyright © SRA/McGraw-Hill

*LESSON* 32 **61**

**6**

She can mend.

Can she mend a sheet?

Can she mend a sock?

She can not mend this.

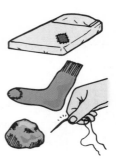

**7**

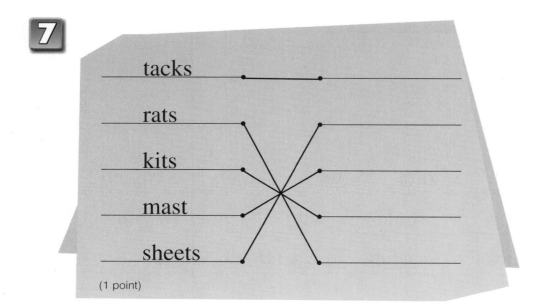

tacks

rats

kits

mast

sheets

(1 point)

**8**

(k)  k c h t l a s k l c h a l s k e t k l s h f i t l a s k d
     h f d k a l d s k d h f  k l t h e d s d s l k d s k e a

(g)  g h i l a s o c i a s d l r i g h d i r e d o s l d i g h
     e i s i a s d o e i a s d f l g l a s i e o a c h d i l g

(sh) s h t h e i s l a i s d f h s d l i a s h d i s l s i d d h
     s i d s h i e l i s f t h e i l s k t s h f i e l s i h s h

(1 point)

| A | B | C |
|---|---|---|

= [ ]

**1**

_____  _____  _____  _____  _____  _____

_____  _____  _____  _____  _____

(1 point)

**2**

1. _____    2. _____    3. _____

4. _____    5. _____    6. _____

(2 points)

**3**

| w̲ish | s̲e̲nt | m̲a̲n | r̲o̲cks | tr̲i̲ms |
|------|------|------|-------|-------|
| w̲in | m̲e̲nd | s̲a̲cks | w̲i̲th | g̲as̲h̲ |
| we̲ | we̲t | sen̲d̲ | m̲e̲n | d̲ash |

**4**

1. We did not get wet feet in the street.

2. She did not see him.

3. Can she see when it is dim?

**5**

1. _____ nee _____    2. _____ at _____    3. _____ ash _____

4. _____ fi _____    5. _____ at _____    6. _____ ca _____

**6**

A cat had wet feet.

Then the cat went in wet sand.

That cat went on a street.

The street has wet sand on it.

**7**

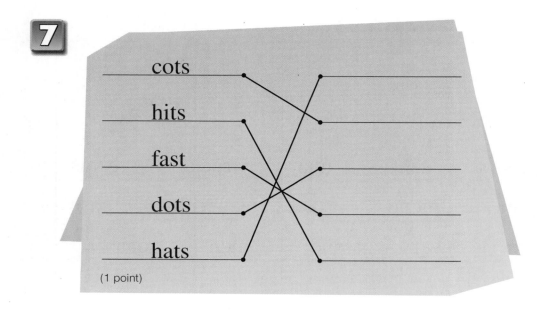

cots

hits

fast

dots

hats

(1 point)

**8**

(on) t o n d m f o n r o n a n d c o n t o n e l a n o s o n s a f l a h o n f h e n o a s o n t h e e n d o n

(he) f r e e h e t h e m e s l f h s a h e s a l f s h e l f l a t a n d m e h e a s t o b e h e f r e e t r e e m e

(she) s h e f l t h e f i a t l i f e s h e f l s d e t h i s h e t r e e s h e l f s k i t h e h e s h e m e t r u e b e

(1 point)

**1**

_____ _____ _____ _____ _____

_____ _____ _____ _____ _____ _____

(1 point)

**2**

1. _____     2. _____     3. _____

4. _____     5. _____     6. _____

(2 points)

**3**

| his | has | ham<u>s</u> | d<u>a</u>sh | d<u>i</u>sh |

| ma<u>sh</u> | ma<u>th</u> | kick<u>s</u> | s<u>a</u>cks | d<u>i</u>d |

| <u>wh</u>en | w<u>i</u>th | <u>r</u><u>o</u>ds | t<u>r</u>ot | <u>s</u>ocks |

**4**

1. She is sad and sick.

2. His fat fish is not fast.

3. She met me at the dam.

**5**

1. ____and____     2. ____an____     3. ____wi____

4. ____fi____     5. ____ma____     6. ____eeds____

The rams had a meet.

This ram can win when the rams trot.

This ram can win when the rams sing.

When can this ram win?

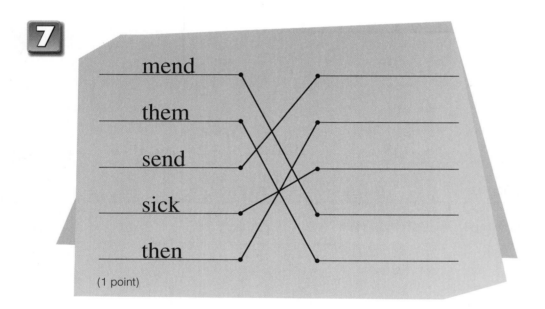

mend

them

send

sick

then

(1 point)

8

me    methesnemenaslemasmenaslnemasremenasmenrlalreremerns

met    setmetmentlretanetandmetfretemetlsmehflaksmetnelkfhetlm

if    riftlskfifhtielifheiasflifhtiilelfitheifhtleilfoshifleifltiefoi

(1 point)

_____ _____ _____ _____ _____

_____ _____ _____ _____ _____

(1 point)

1. _____   2. _____   3. _____

4. _____   5. _____   6. _____

(2 points)

**3**

not        no<u>d</u>s        sh<u>ee</u>ts        ca<u>sh</u>        <u>wheel</u>

t<u>r</u>ees        <u>wh</u>en        s<u>a</u>nd        <u>sh</u>ots        tr<u>i</u>m

<u>d</u>ent        <u>o</u>n        <u>if</u>        <u>in</u>        sen<u>d</u>

**4**

1. The ram will not win the dash.

2. When did that man feed his cats?

3. She got wet in the street.

**5**

1. _____ ca _____   2. _____ fi _____   3. _____ em _____

4. _____ eets _____   5. _____ fi _____   6. _____ and _____

**6**

He has an ant.

That ant is trim and fast.

It is as fast as a cat.

And it can fit in a hand.

**7**

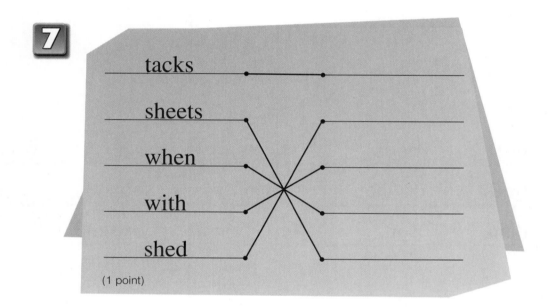

tacks

sheets

when

with

shed

(1 point)

**8**

(it)　itfitlasifilafithfilliasfithfilsfdifhtilealitiflaifltifitfhaisiltif

(we)　werfrelisfaliweflaiwemicilaemcaewalsweilafliweliadfliwerl

(in)　tinsilasmwimasdfilniniasdfliasineiflasidiemafilindiaslimeil
(1 point)

**1**

_____  _____  _____  _____  _____  _____

_____  _____  _____  _____  _____

(1 point)

**2**

1. _____  2. _____  3. _____

4. _____  5. _____  6. _____

(2 points)

**3**

g<u>o</u>t    r<u>a</u>gs    tha<u>n</u>    the<u>m</u>    <u>g</u>et

m<u>a</u>n    m<u>e</u>n    ro<u>ck</u>s    <u>g</u>as    <u>gr</u>im

<u>tr</u>im    w<u>i</u>ll    w<u>e</u>ll

**4**

1. I wish she had ten cats.

2. When he sings, I get sad.

3. That wheel has wet sand on it.

**5**

1. _____ en    2. _____ ca    3. _____ shee

4. _____ th    5. _____ th    6. _____ ca

**6**

A tack sat on the track.

This wheel went on the track.

The tack got in the wheel.

And that wheel did this.

**7**

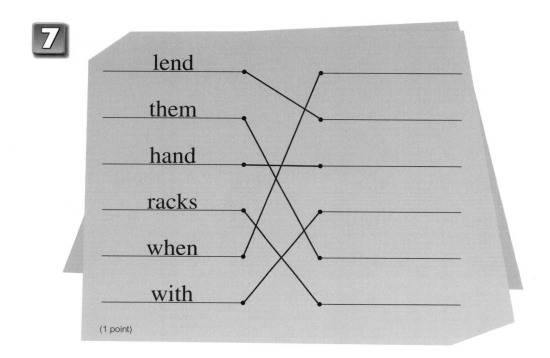

lend

them

hand

racks

when

with

(1 point)

**8**

the | thefedelfthedehtetlthealsifhthelsiftdetlitheslatkeslifhthesl

if | ifthefiltislifitiwisfliwodifltisliftositliasfitdilaidlfifitlaisfi

on | onmeonoameonaosmeonaoeimtoenaosmieoafnoeaoneomafo

(1 point)

| A | B | C | | = | |
|---|---|---|---|---|---|

**1**

_____ _____ _____ _____ _____ _____

_____ _____ _____ _____ _____ _____

(1 point)

**2**

1. _____    2. _____    3. _____

4. _____    5. _____

(2 points)

**3**

meek      mint      hand      c<u>o</u>ld      sol<u>d</u>

<u>sh</u>ell      <u>r</u>acks      c<u>r</u>acks      tr<u>i</u>m      tr<u>ee</u>

tr<u>o</u>d      s<u>l</u>am      s<u>ing</u>      sl<u>e</u>d      sl<u>i</u>d

**4**

1. Ten cats did not feel well.

2. I did not see that shell.

3. Did she see how fast that ant ran?

**5**

1. _____ th _____    2. _____ ick _____    3. _____ fa _____

4. _____ rim _____    5. _____ ca _____    6. _____ ree _____

**6**

A crack is in the street.

A ram is in the crack.

A rat is on the ram.

This is on the rat.

**7**

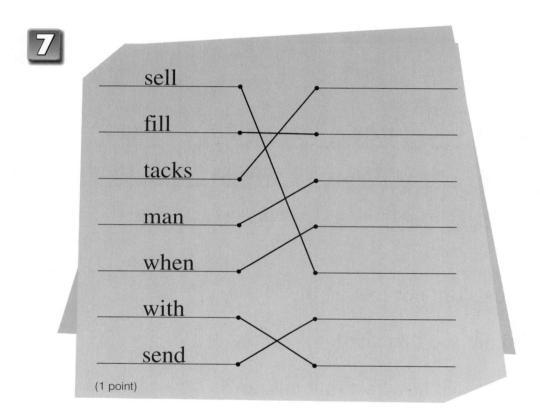

sell

fill

tacks

man

when

with

send

(1 point)

**8**

(she) shethislandskithesheshesdemeheseeshefreesheothesdekneeshes

(the) tnesothattheisthefreetheintnefillshethethefreetheknefeetmethefr

(is) fissthisthelandsithinisthesitlandthisintinthisniclastoisnoti

(1 point)

A  B  C  =

**1**

_____  _____  _____  _____  _____  _____

_____  _____  _____  _____  _____  _____

(1 point)

**2**

1. _____  2. _____  3. _____

4. _____  5. _____

(2 points)

**3**

| <u>l</u>and | w<u>i</u>n | win<u>d</u> | h<u>er</u> | l<u>e</u>nd | lett<u>er</u> | |
| <u>s</u>ell | r<u>e</u>nt | sh<u>e</u> | the<u>m</u> | h<u>o</u>ld | <u>h</u>ill | |
| tha<u>n</u> | s<u>l</u>am | sl<u>i</u>d | sl<u>i</u>m | <u>t</u>old | ha<u>d</u> | <u>h</u>as |

**4**

1. How hot is it in this shack?

2. If the wheel has a dent, it will not go on the track.

3. She slid her sled on the hill.

4. How well can she sing?

**5**

1. _____ha_____  2. _____en_____  3. _____la_____

4. _____ith_____  5. _____rim_____  6. _____ee_____

**6**

A seed sat on a rock.

The seed fell in the sand.

The sand got wet.

A tree is in the sand.

**7**

fist

last

lend

fast

lick

send

(1 point)

**8**

had  radmannadhadshadfadtmahatforhadthehadformethadhasflat

has  thasthatfashasthemasthastraslhashacrashthastlfhasmenthas

is  ifthisbesheisthesthfistshimnisthasthishtsithisthflsisfslsists

(1 point)

A  B  C  □ = □

**1**

_____  _____  _____  _____  _____  _____

_____  _____  _____  _____  _____  _____

(1 point)

**2**

1. _____        2. _____        3. _____

4. _____        5. _____        6. _____

(2 points)

**3**

| her | dig | digge**r** | w**i**n | winne**r** | w**i**th |

| how | ca**s**t | caste**r** | **f**old | dinne**r** | h**a**s |

| tr**ee** | sl**a**m | **p**ack | h**o**ld | th**ing** |

**4**

1. If it is not hot, we will sleep.

2. How did he get so slim?

3. She has a ring on her hand.

4. That cat is slim and sleek.

**5**

1. ____ca____        2. ____end____        3. ____im____

4. ____ha____        5. ____ca____        6. ____ee____

**6**

She went to the shop with her list.

She got socks and sheets and sleds and seeds.

Now she has no cash.

**7**

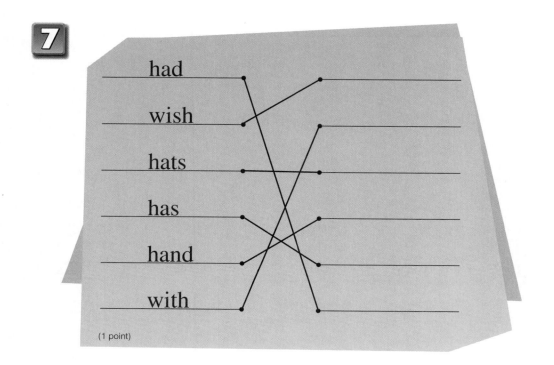

had

wish

hats

has

hand

with

(1 point)

**8**

it   fithinsisitifthehisifthieitfheisitiftheliltithitislitflasitfhiliti

if   riftisflitifitieiflafifitheflaiflsiflelifilasleifiehfiktleifelifltl

an   rantanmannamenamanemananemaeoafnamanefoamanamenfo
(1 point)

**1**

_____  _____  _____  _____  _____  _____

_____  _____  _____  _____  _____

(1 point)

**2**

1. _____  2. _____  3. _____

4. _____  5. _____  6. _____

(2 points)

**3**

pet     petting     win     winner →

winning     sing     singer     letter →

sheep     sleep     slop     slap     slip →

**4**

1. Her pet ram is fat.

2. Will he mend his socks?

3. I am not as sad as I seem.

4. How fast can he go with that cast?

**5**

1. _____ ack     2. _____ sen     3. _____ li

4. _____ ma     5. _____ end     6. _____ ot

**6**

Her dad had a hat.

It did not fit him.

So she got the hat.

It did not fit her.

Now the hat is on her pet pig.

**7**

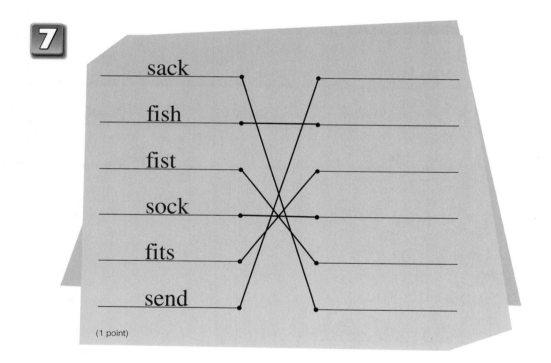

sack

fish

fist

sock

fits

send

(1 point)

**8**

(an) tanfranamenamananamenansmeasoamanamenamsaramanmanrm

(and) randtoanhforamdthelandtlkalandthelamdflakahdlandlalamd

(in) finelsliansimainfielalsmfeinfiemalsfielafnaimainlnlmalftim

(1 point)

A | B | C | | =

**1**

_____ _____ _____ _____ _____ _____

_____ _____ _____ _____ _____ _____

(1 point)

**2**

1. _____ 2. _____ 3. _____

4. _____ 5. _____ 6. _____

(2 points)

**3**

| fill<u>s</u> | fill<u>ing</u> | fill<u>er</u> | fit<u>s</u> | sl<u>a</u>m |

| sla<u>p</u> | s<u>t</u>ep | s<u>t</u>em | ma<u>s</u>t | mast<u>er</u> |

| <u>d</u>own | winn<u>er</u> | c<u>l</u>am | s<u>l</u>eds |

| p<u>o</u>ts | ne<u>ck</u> | f<u>ol</u>d | cra<u>sh</u> |

**4**

1. I sent her a clock last week.

2. Her dad had a hat that fits.

3. If he is not fast, he will lag.

4. She is petting the sheep and singing.

**5**

1. _____ack_____ 2. _____ick_____ 3. _____ha_____

4. _____ee_____ 5. _____sa_____ 6. _____men_____

**6**

His truck has no gas.

So he got a can and went for gas.

He did not get gas.

He had no cash.

So this is how he must get up the hill.

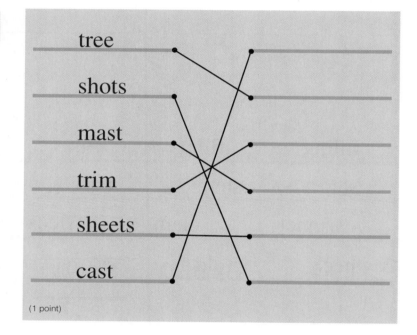

tree

shots

mast

trim

sheets

cast

(1 point)

**8**

she    thisheforsketheshetohedosdeforshetobemesnethesreforshe

shed    thishedheadhadsheddredsderskedtosheddreadshedheadbe

and    grandstandfortheband gothandthemamdtoforandstandabou

(1 point)

**1**

_____ _____ _____ _____ _____ _____

_____ _____ _____ _____ _____ _____

(1 point)

**2**

1. _____     2. _____     3. _____

4. _____     5. _____     6. _____

(2 points)

**3**

rock<u>ing</u>    <u>up</u>    und<u>er</u>    wish<u>ing</u>    send<u>ing</u> →

send<u>er</u>    lett<u>er</u>    s<u>l</u>ams    slap<u>s</u>    pi<u>ck</u>s →

rack<u>s</u>    sl<u>ee</u>p    sadd<u>er</u>    winn<u>ing</u>    m<u>u</u>d →

**4**

1. Meet me on the hill.

2. Has he seen his cat this week?

3. That singer will sing at the dinner.

4. The winner got a gold ring.

**5**

1. ___ist___     2. ___ash___     3. ___la___

4. ___ack___     5. ___its___     6. ___lo___

**6**

The hill is steep.

He will run up the hill.

Then he will rest.

He will not sleep.

He will go down the hill and end up in the mud.

**7**

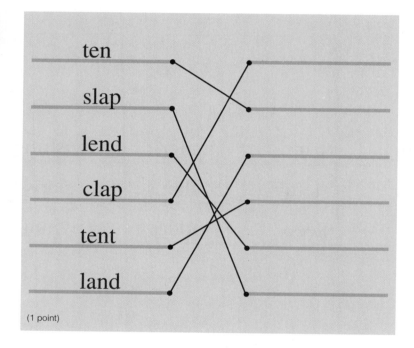

ten

slap

lend

clap

tent

land

(1 point)

**8**

end   trendfenderandindianforendtobendorlendforenhtheemdande

and   tobstandorlandontothesandadneamdnflanhltklandlaskeand

the   forthisistheendofthissheetandtheenditistheseadetlsathaimn
(1 point)

A B C = 

**1**

_____  _____  _____  _____  _____  _____

_____  _____  _____  _____  _____  _____

(1 point)

**2**

1. _____    2. _____

3. _____    4. _____

5. _____    6. _____

7. _____    8. _____

(2 points)

**3**

1. ____ ha ____

2. ____ end ____

3. ____ ack ____

4. ____ pi ____

5. ____ fa ____

6. ____ ish ____

(1 point)

**4**

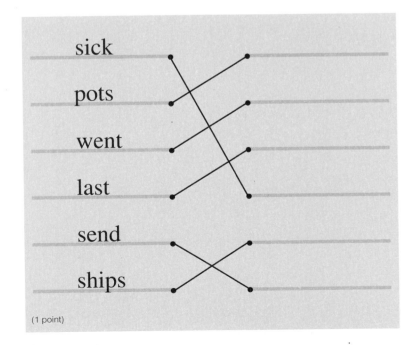

sick

pots

went

last

send

ships

(1 point)

**5**

1. She has a cast on her leg.

2. Is his pet sheep sick?

3. How can she sleep in the sand?

4. This is a fast sled.

5. Send me the clock this week.

6. I get sadder and sadder when she sings.

7. How will we get dinner on this ship?

8. I wish I had ten cats.

 **6**

We fill pots with clams.

We fit lids on the pots.

We can get the pots hot.

That is how we fix a clam dish.

A | B | C | =

**1**

_____ _____ _____ _____ _____ _____

_____ _____ _____ _____ _____ _____

(1 point)

**2**

1. _____  2. _____  3. _____

4. _____  5. _____  6. _____

(2 points)

**3**

| c<u>l</u>am | s<u>l</u>am | m<u>e</u>nd | st<u>re</u>et | f<u>or</u> |
| h<u>a</u>nding | l<u>e</u>nding | c<u>l</u>apping | r<u>ug</u> | the<u>n</u> |
| the<u>m</u> | und<u>er</u> | th<u>a</u>n | g<u>e</u>t | cra<u>sh</u> | c<u>or</u>n |

**4**

1. The old man fell on the dock and got wet.

2. She will fish or sing.

3. Stop filling that gas can with sand.

4. No man will rent that shack.

**5**

1. ___ha___  2. ___ma___  3. ___se___

4. ___eets___  5. ___men___  6. ___and___

He will get up and dig sand.

Then he will run ten laps on the track.

Then he will cut down six trees.

He will go and sleep for a week.

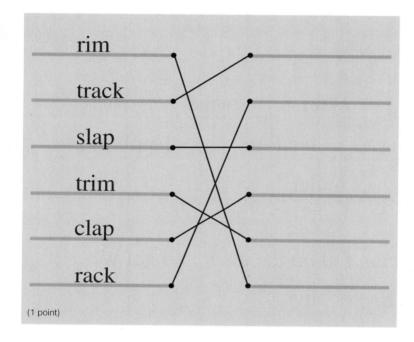

rim

track

slap

trim

clap

rack

(1 point)

(on)  frontandontheendomfromtonthalskehfonaofmsoaienfonaoeia

(an)  fantanfannisthoamaoaonaosdfiansodifoiasmanasdoamasoian

(end) bendtothendslendtheioandoelasdkandelkfendaoisdendlakdne
(1 point)

**1**

_____  _____  _____  _____  _____  _____

_____  _____  _____  _____  _____  _____

(1 point)

**2**

1. _____  2. _____  3. _____

4. _____  5. _____  6. _____

(2 points)

**3**

sleep → rip → grip → trip → slip → he →

be → sander → picker → clams → got →

get → wishing → horn → master → ringing →

**4**

1. His socks fit, but his hat is big.

2. She will sing for the class.

3. That man did not land in the sand.

4. She is trim and fast.

**5**

1. _____ im _____  2. _____ ts _____  3. _____ nd _____

4. _____ cks _____  5. _____ hi _____  6. _____ so _____

She told him to sell the clock.

He went to a shop to sell the clock.

Now he has no clock and no cash.

But he has 3 cats.

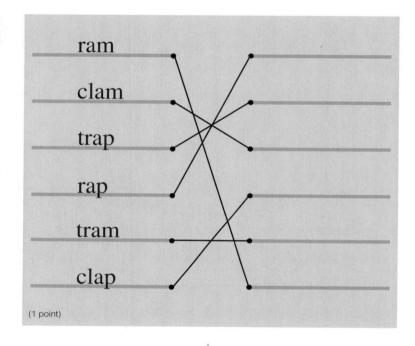

ram

clam

trap

rap

tram

clap

(1 point)

(the) freethesheandhethetretneaksthelaskfuethealstheislfiethea

(then) fortothensheladskethenasdfkltdentlkathenasdthandlkafth

(end) tothesendlaklsdkendlkaskandflkethendltlkehiasdlendlakle

(1 point)

A B C = 

**1**

_____ _____ _____ _____ _____ _____

_____ _____ _____ _____ _____ _____

(1 point)

**2**

1. _____ 2. _____ 3. _____

4. _____ 5. _____ 6. _____

(2 points)

**3**

| | | | | |
|---|---|---|---|---|
| t<u>r</u>im | <u>g</u>rim | <u>g</u>rip | <u>gr</u>een | h<u>o</u>ld |
| <u>gr</u><u>a</u>ss | c<u>l</u>ass | cl<u>o</u>ck | t<u>r</u>ip | s<u>l</u>ip |
| s<u>l</u>eep | <u>sh</u>eep | sh<u>i</u>p | h<u>o</u>rn | send<u>in</u>g |
| s<u>o</u> | b<u>or</u>n | c<u>o</u>t | c<u>o</u>lt | <u>s</u>old | <u>for</u> |

**4**

1. I am not a big winner.

2. He will lend us his tent.

3. When can I meet that man?

4. We will clap if she sings well.

**5**

1. _____ st _____ 2. _____ ts _____ 3. _____ ha _____

4. _____ ot _____ 5. _____ si _____ 6. _____ en _____

**6**

That clock is running fast.

It is set for 8.

But it will ring when it is 4.

The man will get up when the clock rings.

But he will not be glad.

**7**

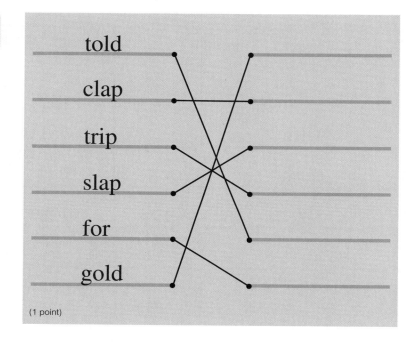

told

clap

trip

slap

for

gold

(1 point)

 **8**

(on) t o n f o m e u n e m a o n e a o e m a o e n f a o a o n e o a c n a o e n c n e o n a o e o a o m a

(no) t o b e o n a o n o a o a o e m a o f m a n o a o e m a n o f a m a o f n o a o e a o n o c a n e o

(ant) r a n t a n d t h e l a n d a m a n t l a l k e k f a n t l a l f k e h a k d l e c l d a a n t l e k a n h a l

(1 point)

**1**

_____  _____  _____  _____  _____  _____

_____  _____  _____  _____  _____  _____

(1 point)

**2**

1. _____   2. _____   3. _____

4. _____   5. _____   6. _____

(2 points)

**3**

yell    finger    sadder    master    fishing

sled    slid    bell    sander    sender

gold    mud    flaps    letter

**4**

1. We met her at the creek.

2. Is she swimming in the pond?

3. When will the bell ring?

4. She had dinner with us last week.

**5**

1. ____ee____   2. ____fa____   3. ____ug____

4. ____co____   5. ____old____   6. ____li____

**6**

We will go fishing.

A big fish is in the creek.

If we get that fish, we will pop it in a pan.

Then we will have a big fish for dinner.

**7**

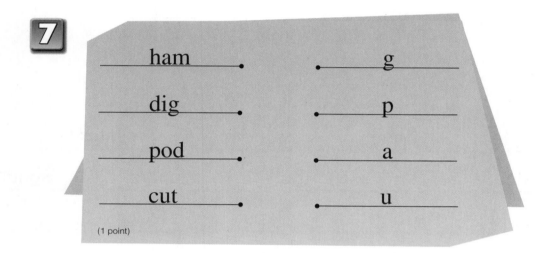

| | |
|---|---|
| ham | g |
| dig | p |
| pod | a |
| cut | u |

(1 point)

**8**

has    i a s h a s h a d o h i d h a s i s f i s f a s h a c h a s t h i s i s h i s h a s h o d h a d h a s f a s t i s

hand    l a n d h a n d h a d f a d f a n h a n d s a n d s t a n d h a n d l a n d f a n l a n t a d h a n d m

no    n o t o r o n n o a n i n o n t o n a n o t o r m o r m o n o c n i n a n o n i s h o n a r o t o n o t o

(1 point)

**1**

_____ _____ _____ _____ _____

_____ _____ _____ _____ _____

(1 point)

**2**

1. _____  2. _____  3. _____  4. _____

5. _____  6. _____  7. _____  8. _____

(2 points)

**3**

1. _____lo_____  2. _____ca_____  3. _____end_____

4. _____eep_____  5. _____ip_____  6. _____or_____

(1 point)

**4**

sock •        • a

clap •        • m

will •        • k

must •        • i

(1 point)

1. The black colt will trot on the track.

2. Her hat fits, but her wig is big.

3. The class will end with a test.

4. The bell will ring for dinner.

5. The flag is old and torn.

6. The fox is running up the steep hill.

7. Send him six green sheets.

She will lend us a big tent.

We will go on a trip.

We will swim in the pond.

Then we will set up the tent on a hill.

And we will sleep in it.

A  B  C  =  

**1**

_____  _____  _____  _____  _____  _____

_____  _____  _____  _____  _____  _____

(1 point)

**2**

1. _____   2. _____   3. _____   4. _____

5. _____   6. _____   7. _____   8. _____

(2 points)

**3**

1. _____ se _____   2. _____ ack _____   3. _____ ut _____

4. _____ orn _____   5. _____ pe _____   6. _____ ip _____

(1 point)

**4**

but •          • i

yes •          • f

dig •          • s

for •          • u

(1 point)

1. How can we fix the truck?

2. Her cat is sleeping in her bed.

3. The swimming class went well.

4. See me sleep in the green grass.

5. Keep sending me happy letters.

6. Now I will cut down six trees.

7. When can we swim at the creek?

8. She left us and got on the bus.

A ram was sick.

Six sheep sent him a greeting.

The sheep sent him a big dinner and a gift.

Now he is happy, but he is still sick.

**1**

_____  _____  _____  _____  _____  _____

_____  _____  _____  _____  _____  _____

(1 point)

**2**

1. _____  2. _____  3. _____

4. _____  5. _____  6. _____

(2 points)

**3**

| p<u>i</u>ts | und<u>er</u> | wish<u>ing</u> | c<u>or</u>n | morn<u>ing</u> |
|---|---|---|---|---|
| f<u>i</u>lls | h<u>er</u> | p<u>e</u>cks | p<u>ee</u>ks | st<u>ree</u>t |
| g<u>r</u>ass | greet<u>s</u> | sl<u>e</u>d | cl<u>u</u>b | last<u>ing</u> |

**4**

1. How can he sleep when we sing?

2. If she is sick, I will send her a greeting.

3. When will she meet us for dinner?

4. The math class did not go well.

**5**

1. _____ b _____  2. _____ mu _____  3. _____ fo _____

4. _____ ip _____  5. _____ se _____  6. _____ ag _____

6

An ant sat in wet sand.

A man dug in that sand for clams.

The man got 37 clams and 1 wet ant.

That ant and the man had a clam dinner.

7

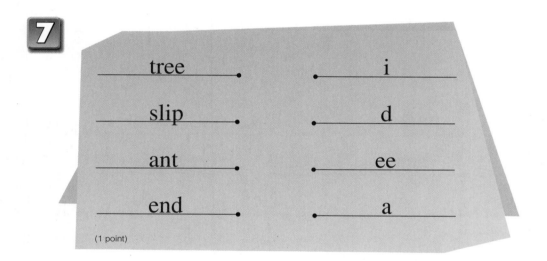

tree • • i

slip • • d

ant • • ee

end • • a

(1 point)

8

(us) u p a s i s u s u n s u s u o r u n u s a s i s h i s h u s f u s s u n i s a s u p u n u s n s a s i s n

(send) e n d s n e d e s e n t s e n d e n d s e n t s e m d t h e n s e n d r e n d s e n t s e n d e r a n d

(or) f o r o n u s o f t o o r o n n o r f r o n t o f o r o m s o n s o r e f o r m o s t l o n o r t r o n d

(1 point)

**1**

_____ _____ _____ _____ _____ _____

_____ _____ _____ _____ _____ _____

(1 point)

**2**

1. _____     2. _____     3. _____

4. _____     5. _____     6. _____

7. _____

(2 points)

**3**

best          west          p<u>a</u>th          f<u>e</u>lt →

c<u>o</u>ld          c<u>or</u>n          dr<u>o</u>p          dr<u>i</u>p          bl<u>a</u>ck →

gr<u>ee</u>ts          cl<u>u</u>b          bo<u>x</u>          h<u>a</u>ppy →

**4**

1. She trots faster than the sheep.

2. How can ten men fit in that tent?

3. When they met, they felt happy.

4. When will they stop sending me letters?

**5**

1. ___sl___  2. ___wh___

2. ___la___  4. ___ru___

5. ___an___  6. ___eep___

**6**

The sun was hot.

A pig went on a dusty path.

A cat was in a tree.

It was not hot in the tree.

But a pig can not go up a tree.

So the pig got in the mud.

Now the pig is happy.

**7**

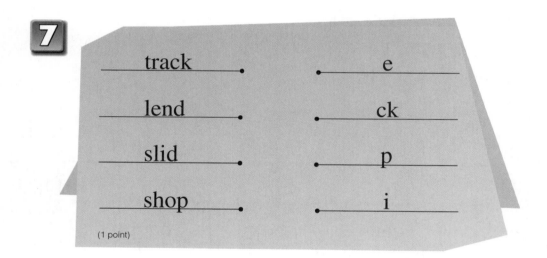

___track___ •          • ___e___

___lend___ •          • ___ck___

___slid___ •          • ___p___

___shop___ •          • ___i___

(1 point)

**8**

(the) thatthehishethefreehethethisthatthemthanthethashehethefe

(and) antandendsandfendtrandlendantamdsamtsardandlondtrantla

(she) seepsheetseemshoresheshareshadsheenshashoasheshcseemsh

(1 point)

| A | B | C |
|---|---|---|

= 

**1**

_____ _____ _____ _____ _____ _____

_____ _____ _____ _____ _____ _____

(1 point)

**2**

1. _____   2. _____   3. _____

4. _____   5. _____   6. _____

7. _____

(2 points)

**3**

gripp<u>ing</u>      <u>sh</u>ops      <u>ch</u>ops      bu<u>s</u>t      und<u>er</u>

p<u>ee</u>ks      d<u>u</u>sty      la<u>n</u>ds      tr<u>u</u>ck      t<u>e</u>nt      la<u>p</u>s

clapp<u>ing</u>      cl<u>i</u>pp<u>ing</u>      m<u>or</u>ning      bo<u>x</u>      m<u>o</u>ld

**4**

1. They will lock the shed in the morning.

2. Then she told me how happy she was.

3. That bug was green and black.

4. Did she go to the store yet?

5. How did that clock get a dent in it?

**5**

1. _____ sl _____    2. _____ mu _____    3. _____ co _____

4. _____ im _____    5. _____ la _____    6. _____ eep _____

**6**

Ten men got in a truck.

They went to the creek and set up a tent.

How can ten men fit in the tent?

They can not.

Six men will sleep under a tree.

**7**

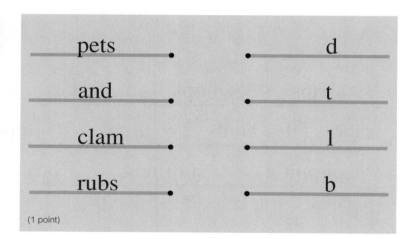

| pets | · | · | d |
|---|---|---|---|
| and | · | · | t |
| clam | · | · | l |
| rubs | · | · | b |

(1 point)

**8**

(then) tenhenthenthemhemtenhenthenthethattheythenthethanthent

(he) henhathehashishihohehahentenmenfencehenthanshathanheb

(had) hashathashadhavehashedheadhashadhamfadsadhadmaddadh

(1 point)

**1**

_____ _____ _____ _____ _____

_____ _____ _____ _____ _____ _____

(1 point)

**2**

1. _____  2. _____  3. _____

4. _____  5. _____  6. _____

7. _____

(2 points)

**3**

1. ___amp___   2. ___olt___   3. ___s___

4. ___sl___   5. ___ey___   6. ___ye___

(1 point)

**4**

| short | • | • | ch |
| sold | • | • | th |
| much | • | • | or |
| bath | • | • | ol |

(1 point)

## 5

1. He said, "I will go to the store."

2. She told him, "Go rent a truck."

3. They said, "We had fun on the trip."

## 6

1. Next week, we will plant six seeds.

2. Send me a better letter.

3. On the trip, I got sick.

4. For lunch, they had fish and chips.

## 7

She told him, "Let us go on a clipper ship."

But he had no cash. He said, "We will pan for gold."

So they went to the hills. Then they went on that clipper ship.

**1**

_____  _____  _____  _____  _____  _____

_____  _____  _____  _____  _____  _____

(1 point)

**2**

1. _____    2. _____    3. _____

4. _____    5. _____    6. _____

7. _____

(2 points)

**3**

chip　　sand　　bent　　rents　　big

bug　　gripping　　help　　need　　they

silly　　for　　now　　mats　　slug　　rag

**4**

1. He said, "I will win the meet."

2. She said, "Fix the casters on that bed."

3. The clock was running faster.

4. We went and sat under the tree.

5. If we rent a truck, we can go on a trip.

**5**

1. _____ co _____  2. _____ im _____  3. _____ sa _____

4. _____ t _____  5. _____ nd _____  6. _____ d _____

**6**

The dog was wet and muddy. Ted said, "That dog
needs a bath." Ann said, "Get a rag." Ted did that.
So the dog got a bath. But Ann and Ted got
wet and muddy.

**7**

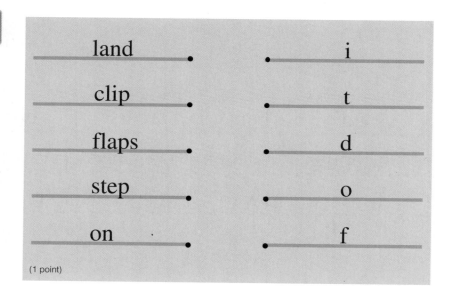

| | |
|---|---|
| land | i |
| clip | t |
| flaps | d |
| step | o |
| on | f |

(1 point)

**8**

(be) m e h e b e t h e b e s e h e s h e t h e t h a t b e o r b a b y b o y b y b e b u m t h e d e n e h

(up) u p o r u g f o r u p o n t h e h u g o t h e r u p u f u h e u y r u g t o u p t h e d u d h u g h u

(when) t h e n w h e n w h o t h a t t h a n w h a t w h e n w h e r e w h e n w h a n t h e w e n h n w

(1 point)

**1**

_____ _____ _____ _____ _____ _____

_____ _____ _____ _____ _____ _____

(1 point)

**2**

1. _____   2. _____   3. _____

4. _____   5. _____   6. _____

(2 points)

**3**

wheel   well   bump   clamp   bold

yet   self   shelf   bath   such   felt

morning   dripping   muddy   next   better

**4**

1. On the next morning, he felt happy.

2. She said, "Was the cat sleeping under the bed?"

3. We do not sit in wet sand.

4. Help that man lift this box.

5. If the sheet is torn, we will mend it.

6. At last, she got socks that fit.

1. _____ le _____ 2. _____ amp _____ 3. _____ en _____

4. _____ eep _____ 5. _____ eep _____ 6. _____ em _____

A horse met a sheep. The horse said, "I can trot faster than a sheep." The sheep got mad. Then the horse said, "And I can swim faster than a sheep." The sheep said, "But I can do this better than a horse." The sheep went to sleep.

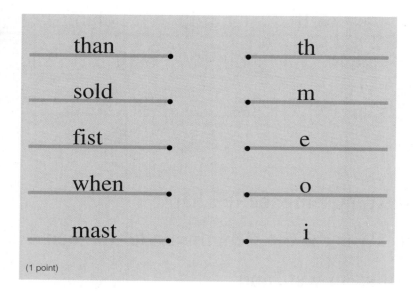

| | |
|---|---|
| than | th |
| sold | m |
| fist | e |
| when | o |
| mast | i |

(1 point)

(when) thenwhenwhowhenthatwhatthenwhentobeenwhemthewentht

(if) tifthisifistobeitcandoidinanaforiftoisitihifitisaninifinana

(she) theshehebefreeshetobehemetheshethishasteshethemeshefr

(1 point)

**1**

_____  _____  _____  _____  _____

_____  _____  _____  _____  _____

(1 point)

**2**

1. _____    2. _____    3. _____

4. _____    5. _____    6. _____

7. _____

(2 points)

**3**

next     drops     wet     greets     champs

dump     went     slips     much

mister     folding     clock     under     greeting

**4**

1. Go to the flag and stand still.

2. The tracks led to a shack next to the hill.

3. If she can dig, she can plant this tree.

4. Was she picking up jam at the store?

5. How much cash do they need?

**5**

1. _____lls_____   2. _____eep_____   3. _____ap_____

4. _____en_____   5. _____fee_____   6. _____la_____

**6**

Ann was a winner on the track. And she was the best singer in town. She said to her self, "I need cash. I can get a job running or a job singing." She got the best job. She is the singer at track meets, and she is glad.

**7**

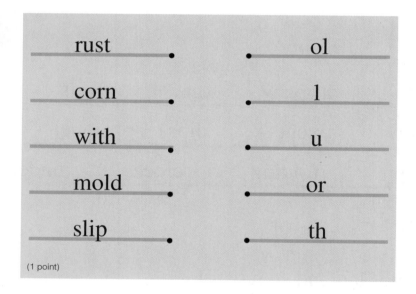

rust      ol

corn      l

with      u

mold      or

slip      th

(1 point)

**8**

(not) tonornotnobnotomotnofnodnotnornodnofnobnotontoreornoe

(be) mehefeebeteethebeheshethebemebathebetmetmenbanbeambo

(an) tanconfromamanoninanamonomiminantinamantmentenantan

(1 point)

**1**

_____  _____  _____  _____  _____  _____

_____  _____  _____  _____  _____  _____

(1 point)

**2**

1. _____   2. _____   3. _____

4. _____   5. _____   6. _____

7. _____

(2 points)

**3**

clash     lift     west     lunch     singer

flip     slipping     rust     crust     north

licks     winning     jumps     champ     clamp

1. He told me, "Do not go to class."

2. How steep is that hill?

3. We must plant more corn seeds.

4. Do they need help with that horse?

5. How fast can she cut the grass?

6. She said, "Do not set that pen on the desk."

**5**

1. _____ fi _____    2. _____ th _____    3. _____ en _____

4. _____ ca _____    5. _____ we _____    6. _____ ip _____

**6**

Bud and Al went on a trip. Al said, "We will stop for lunch."
They sat on a hill next to the pond. They did not see that
the hill was an ant hill. The ants got cold cuts and chips.
Al got ants in his pants.

**7**

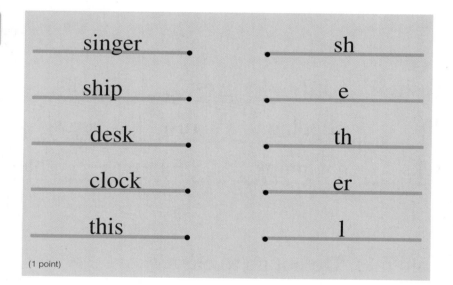

singer · · sh

ship · · e

desk · · th

clock · · er

this · · l

(1 point)

**8**

(in) oninanmantantindandimdindonaninanonmanmadmidtinfanla

(it) ifitihitthistoifihnlittlerisitinatoranratfantinasitisifitisanth

(was) sawcandowaswantthatwhatwhasawmanwasthatwantwaswan

(1 point)

A B C = 

**1**

_____ _____ _____ _____ _____ _____

_____ _____ _____ _____ _____ _____

(1 point)

**2**

1. _____    2. _____    3. _____

4. _____    5. _____    6. _____

7. _____    8. _____

(2 points)

**3**

| | | | | |
|---|---|---|---|---|
| rest | winning | pants | clash | rushing |
| better | telling | thing | path | colt |
| think | swimmer | sacks | bother | much |

**4**

1. Did you see six black bugs under the rug?

2. Now it is sunny, so we can swim.

3. Go to the next class as fast as you can.

4. What do they see on the bus?

5. They said, "We will plant the last of the seeds."

**5**

1. _____ ca _____ 2. _____ hi _____ 3. _____ im _____

4. _____ ip _____ 5. _____ ro _____ 6. _____ ab _____

**6**

He said, "We must get a gift for Pam." She said, "We can get her a green frog or a pet fish." "No," he said. "We will get her a black cat or a big horse." She said, "That is silly. We can not get her a horse." So they got her a colt.

**7**

| | |
|---|---|
| trap • | • ee |
| short • | • ap |
| beet • | • g |
| fold • | • ol |
| dents • | • nt |
| go • | • or |

(1 point)

**8**

chip   shipchipchopchapchipchinchanshipchimchapchopchipchisls

was   sawantascanwasseewastetobeasintoforwashaswantwhatwasi

no   oninanoeisantoaienoaneoafaioeansfmenafmenoaiemfonameo

(1 point)

| A | B | C |
|---|---|---|

= 

**1**

_____  _____  _____  _____  _____

_____  _____  _____  _____  _____

(1 point)

**2**

1. _____  2. _____  3. _____

4. _____  5. _____  6. _____

7. _____  8. _____

(2 points)

**3**

th<u>ing</u>s  run<u>s</u>  c<u>l</u>ips  both<u>er</u>  ⟶

lun<u>ch</u>  y<u>e</u>lls  d<u>ee</u>p  de<u>s</u>k  b<u>o</u>lt ⟶

sw<u>ing</u>  r<u>e</u>nt  <u>ch</u>eck  pin<u>n</u>ing  s<u>e</u>lf ⟶

**4**

1. If he is happy, he will slap us on the back.

2. Do you need to go to town?

3. See that horse run on a dusty path.

4. Do you smell the jam?

5. What do you do in the morning?

6. "Hand me the pen," she said.

7. What gift was she wishing for?

**5**

1. _____ dr _____    2. _____ ee _____    3. _____ ma _____    4. _____ ink _____

5. _____ le _____    6. _____ op _____    7. _____ fi _____

**6**

He told me how to get to the best store in town. He told me to go left at the gift shop and go north. He said, "Then you will go six blocks to the west." He said, "Then go up the hill and down the next street." Do you think I got to the store? No. I got lost.

**7**

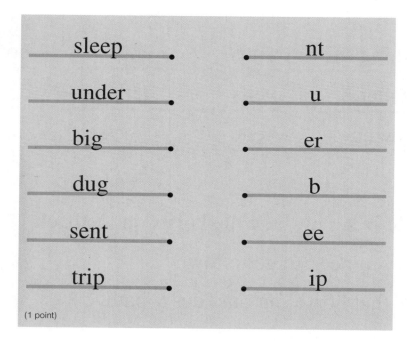

| sleep | | nt |
| under | | u |
| big | | er |
| dug | | b |
| sent | | ee |
| trip | | ip |

(1 point)

**8**

(when) thenthanwhenwhattheythanwhanwhenthethiswhatwhentothe

(to) itistoofhotheonethletoshflaofhsthotatontoforistheforti otofh

(has) hishamhashimherhashcantrashishisforhashamandhisfastobe

(1 point)

**1**

_____ _____ _____ _____ _____ _____

_____ _____ _____ _____ _____ _____

(1 point)

**2**

1. _____   2. _____   3. _____

4. _____   5. _____   6. _____

7. _____   8. _____

(2 points)

**3**

feels    letters    blush    crush    jelly

funny    greeting    lunch    mold

ringing    next    west    store    very

**4**

1. He said, "What can I do so that you will feel better?"

2. What was she picking on top of the hill?

3. They had lots of desks in the class.

4. She said, "Stand still or you will slip."

5. What will you get when you go to the store?

# LESSON 60

**5**

1. ____am____   2. ____ip____   3. ____an____

4. ____ho____   5. ____eeps____   6. ____we____

**6**

We had a clock that did not run. We went to a clock fixer and said,
"Can you fix this clock?" He said, "Yes, I can get it to run."
The next morning, we went back to pick up the clock. The old man
held up the clock. He said, "I stuck legs on the clock.
Now it will run."

**7**

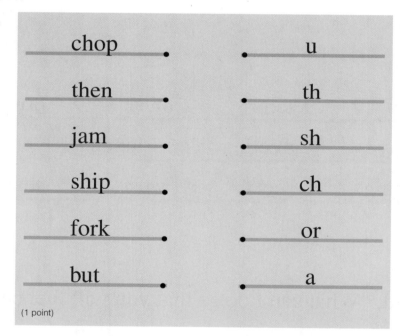

| chop | • | • | u |
| then | • | • | th |
| jam | • | • | sh |
| ship | • | • | ch |
| fork | • | • | or |
| but | • | • | a |

(1 point)

**8**

(to) forothotoformhastobeholdcoldorhastobeinthetoitoftheoffoh

(ship) shifthishipintoshoresirshinerohtheshipishapelyshipshopchi

(was) sawthewhatwashetherehasmastobenwasawaythenasmashedh

(1 point)

LESSON **61**

| A | B | C |     | = |     |
|---|---|---|---|---|---|

## 1

_____ _____ _____ _____ _____ _____

_____ _____ _____ _____ _____

(1 point)

## 2

1. _____   2. _____   3. _____

4. _____   5. _____   6. _____

7. _____

(2 points)

## 3

1. ____ju____   2. ____eck____   3. ____sho____

4. ____ell____   5. ____cla____   6. ____re____

(1 point)

## 4

chip •        • x

horn •        • a

jump •        • r

was •         • u

next •        • i

(1 point)

1. Do you think we can go swimming if it gets sunny?

2. Check with the man at the desk.

3. What did they do after dinner?

4. Did she keep her hands on the wheel?

5. You can not do math as well as I can.

An old truck did not stop well. Sandy got in the truck and went to the top of a steep hill. Then she went down the hill faster and faster. She said, "I do not think I can stop this truck." A pond was at the end of the street. Now Sandy is sitting in a wet truck with six frogs.

**1**

_____  _____  _____  _____  _____  _____

_____  _____  _____  _____  _____  _____

(1 point)

**2**

1. _____   2. _____   3. _____

4. _____   5. _____   6. _____

7. _____   8. _____

(2 points)

**3**

dust      very      b<u>i</u>g      d<u>i</u>g      b<u>u</u>st      bun<u>s</u>

left      su<u>ch</u>      butt<u>er</u>      b<u>a</u>tter      send<u>er</u>

fold<u>er</u>      l<u>u</u>cky      f<u>ee</u>ling      c<u>r</u>ush      fl<u>a</u>gs

**4**

1. How did so much dust get on the plants?

2. She said, "We can get more chips at the store."

3. You left lots of things on her desk.

4. What did she do when she felt bad?

5. After dinner, we will sit on the swing.

**5**

1. _____ op _____  2. _____ th _____  3. _____ ha _____

4. _____ st _____  5. _____ nt _____  6. _____ d _____

**6**

Ann went to the bun shop with her mixer. She said, "With this batter mixer, I can fix the best batter." "No," the men said. "We fix the best batter. It has the best butter." She said, "Mix the best butter with this batter mixer." So they did. They got the best buns in town.

**7**

| | |
|---|---|
| ship | ck |
| sold | ch |
| chip | ee |
| tubs | sh |
| locks | u |
| creek | ol |

(1 point)

**8**

(end)  lendthandhenhandcanendsentforlendthenhasandtoendsadn

(much)  suchgoodmuchcanshouldmochormuchtouchatmuchhutchca

(on)  tonforaninamonemaosoemaosnaoeoonasinanimonomamom

(1 point)

A  B  C  =  

**1**

_____  _____  _____  _____  _____  _____

_____  _____  _____  _____  _____  _____

(1 point)

**2**

1. _____   2. _____   3. _____

4. _____   5. _____   6. _____

7. _____   8. _____

(2 points)

**3**

d<u>o</u>cks    hamm<u>er</u>    <u>ch</u>amp    chopp<u>ing</u>    <u>sh</u>opping

b<u>u</u>nch    sw<u>ee</u>t    v<u>e</u>ry    jun<u>k</u>    butt<u>er</u>

bo<u>th</u>er    cr<u>u</u>sh    h<u>e</u>ld    stu<u>ck</u>    sw<u>ing</u>ing

**4**

1. When will we get to the top of the hill?

2. What will we fix for dinner?

3. How well do you sleep in this tent?

4. That jam is very red and sweet.

5. They had to do the planting in the spring.

6. She was yelling, "Stop that bus."

**5**

1. _____ eep     2. _____ t     3. _____ l

4. _____ h     5. _____ w     6. _____ b

**6**

Her mom told her, "The street is slick." But she went in the street with her slippers. The slippers did not grip the street. She fell on her back. Her mom said, "I told you it was slick." She said, "Yes, I just went slipping in my slippers."

**7**

| | |
|---|---|
| much • | • or |
| tells • | • m |
| slams • | • g |
| lunch • | • ll |
| form • | • a |
| bugs • | • l |

(1 point)

**8**

(chop)  shopthechopthesoshipchipchopshipchopshopchinshinchip

(do)  todoofhothedomeisotopordoorcandoitorfrotheendtodowho

(this)  thisishisshipasthisisthatornotthinforthesthisasthinhisthi

(1 point)

**1**

_____ _____ _____ _____ _____

_____ _____ _____ _____ _____

(1 point)

**2**

1. _____      2. _____      3. _____

4. _____      5. _____      6. _____

7. _____      8. _____

(2 points)

**3**

tub      quit      mixer      which      stuck →

vest      sitting      checks      vet      shops →

lucky      chip      shelf      tell      till      skunk →

**4**

1. If I ask, he will lend me his vest.

2. You can chop lots of nuts with that mixer.

3. Which cat sat on this desk?

4. His mom said, "Stop sitting on that stump."

5. It was sunny on top of this hill.

# LESSON 64

**5**

1. ___d___     2. ___m___     3. ___h___

4. ___p___     5. ___p___     6. ___p___

**6**

After lunch, Pam and her dad went to the vet with a sick frog. They sat down next to a man that had a skunk. Pam said to the man, "Can I pet that skunk?" The man said, "Do not bother this skunk. Or you will smell a big stink." Just then, the frog went hop, hop. And what do you think that skunk did?

**7**

| | |
|---|---|
| tipping | tt |
| better | j |
| singer | pp |
| just | er |
| clocks | ch |
| such | cks |

(1 point)

**8**

(much) suchmuchtouchhutchsuchmuchmichorsickmochtouchmuchso

(then) whenthenhenthanthatwhenwhatthenasthemorthanthenthemt

(bad) hadtosadofbadthesadbadhadhatbatcanhadbadhatcanbantoda

(1 point)

**1**

_____ _____ _____ _____ _____ _____

_____ _____ _____ _____ _____ _____

(1 point)

**2**

1. _____   2. _____   3. _____

4. _____   5. _____   6. _____

7. _____   8. _____

(2 points)

**3**

very        self        green        clips        block

glass        slipper        stump        shell        path

clamp        quick        mister        dust        flips

**4**

1. What did she do with the truck?

2. Her dad told her, "Send me a letter."

3. You will feel happy when that horse wins.

4. Which slippers will fit on this shelf?

5. The old man said, "That sink is not for drinking."

6. Will you ask her how much the rent is?

**5**

1. _____ ee _____   2. _____ f _____

3. _____ m _____   4. _____ d _____

5. _____ p _____   6. _____ p _____

7. _____ ca _____

**6** A green frog was in a bath tub. A red bug said, "Can I get in the tub with you?" "No," the frog said. "This tub is for me." The bug said, "But I need a bath." The frog said, "Go hop in the sink." That is what the bug did. It went for a swim in the sink.

**7**

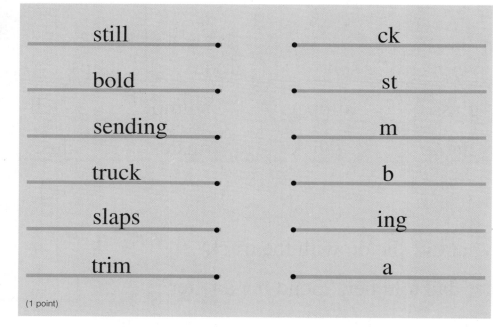

still · · ck

bold · · st

sending · · m

truck · · b

slaps · · ing

trim · · a

(1 point)

**8**

(do) todoofthetomodoefoaofodoaoeofmdogoadleidohdowohodoelg

(bad) sadhadbadcaddadasanaddfadbadsadtheladhadasadbadcadha

(was) sawasasawarcancawarmasthatwasawforwashingthewasitfast

(1 point)